The Open University

Open Mathematics

Unit 9

Music

MU120 course units were produced by the following team:

Gaynor Arrowsmith (Course Manager)

Mike Crampin (Author)

Margaret Crowe (Course Manager)

Fergus Daly (Academic Editor)

Judith Daniels (Reader)

Chris Dillon (Author)

Judy Ekins (Chair and Author)

John Fauvel (Academic Editor)

Barrie Galpin (Author and Academic Editor)

Alan Graham (Author and Academic Editor)

Linda Hodgkinson (Author)

Gillian Iossif (Author)

Joyce Johnson (Reader)

Eric Love (Academic Editor)

Kevin McConway (Author)

David Pimm (Author and Academic Editor)

Karen Rex (Author)

Other contributions to the text were made by a number of Open University staff and students and others acting as consultants, developmental testers, critical readers and writers of draft material. The course team are extremely grateful for their time and effort.

The course units were put into production by the following:

Course Materials Production Unit (Faculty of Mathematics and Computing)

Martin Brazier (Graphic Designer)	Diane Mole (Graphic Designer)
Hannah Brunt (Graphic Designer)	Kate Richenburg (Publishing Editor)
Alison Cadle (TEXOpS Manager)	John A.Taylor (Graphic Artist)
Jenny Chalmers (Publishing Editor)	Howie Twiner (Graphic Artist)
Sue Dobson (Graphic Artist)	Nazlin Vohra (Graphic Designer)
Roger Lowry (Publishing Editor)	Steve Rycroft (Publishing Editor)

This publication forms part of an Open University course. Details of this and other Open University courses can be obtained from the Student Registration and Enquiry Service, The Open University, PO Box 197, Milton Keynes MK7 6BJ, United Kingdom: tel. +44 (0)845 300 6090, email general-enquiries@open.ac.uk

Alternatively, you may visit the Open University website at http://www.open.ac.uk where you can learn more about the wide range of courses and packs offered at all levels by The Open University.

To purchase a selection of Open University course materials visit http://www.ouw.co.uk, or contact Open University Worldwide, Walton Hall, Milton Keynes MK7 6AA, United Kingdom, for a brochure: tel. +44 (0)1908 858793, fax +44 (0)1908 858787, email ouw-customer-services@open.ac.uk

The Open University, Walton Hall, Milton Keynes, MK7 6AA.

First published 1996. Second edition 2000. Third edition 2008.

Edited, designed and typeset by The Open University, using the Open University TEX System.

Printed and bound in the United Kingdom by The Charlesworth Group, Wakefield.

ISBN 978 0 7492 2867 5

3.1

Contents

Study guide

This unit is written in four sections. Sections 1 to 3 deal with musical themes. In order to emphasize the links with mathematics, these sections are structured around various key questions that are often asked in relation to music. In particular:

◇   What sort of tune is this?

◇   What is a musical note?

◇   Why do certain notes sound pleasing together?

◇   Why are there twelve notes in a Western musical scale?

Section 4 summarizes and draws together the key ideas presented in Block B, especially emphasizing algebra, graphs and calculator work. You may need to use *Resource Book B* in conjunction with this section.

The *Calculator Book* is integrated into your study of Sections 1, 3 and 4.

There is a video band associated with Section 1, and an audio to go with Section 3.

In addition, there is a television programme linked to the unit: *A Language for Movement*, which looks at a variety of forms of dance and musical notation.

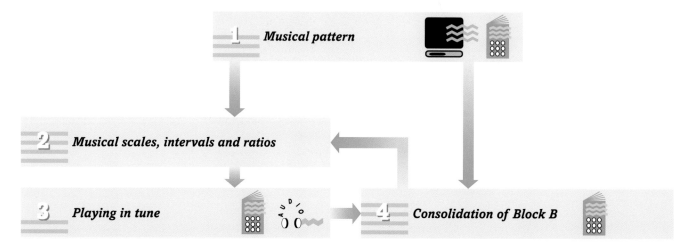

Summary of sections and other course components needed for *Unit 9*.

Introduction

The central theme of this unit is musical pattern and how it can be visualized and also represented on paper. Within the enjoyable context of music, you will find that mathematical thinking can contribute fresh ways of seeing, hearing and appreciating something artistic. Some music lovers may feel uneasy about exposing music to the mathematician's analytical eye. However, the mathematical ideas presented here are aimed at enhancing musical experience, not diminishing it.

In the visual arts, beauty has to do with recognizing, perhaps subconsciously, subtle patterns and structures. The same is true in music. But there are three features peculiar to music that make musical patterns difficult to analyse. Firstly, the essence of music is aural—it is experienced through the ears rather than through the eyes. Secondly, a musical event is experienced over time—it cannot be appreciated in an instant. And finally, a feature of live music is that it is transitory—once experienced, it has gone, apart from the memory and the pleasure of the experience. Therefore, music is difficult to analyse because it is *aural, temporal* and *transitory*.

In order to appreciate musical patterns and to study these structures in more depth, it is necessary to find a way of pinning music down either in pictures or by means of some form of written notation. This is where *mathematics* comes in. As you will already be aware from studying previous units, mathematics is strong on providing written notation as well as helpful diagrams and graphs. In this unit you will therefore be encouraged to 'picture' musical patterns; hence the unit fits in with the theme of this block—'Every picture tells a story'.

This is a *mathematics* unit, not a *musical* one. You will not be expected to know any musical theory nor will you be tested on your knowledge of music. It does not matter if you feel that you are 'unmusical'—you can still do the unit! You may find the Musical Glossary at the back of the unit useful if you come across any unfamiliar musical terms.

The unit is entitled 'Music', and although the emphasis is on mathematics, it tries to convey a strong sense of musical enjoyment. It will help if you can engage with the music and enjoy it, particularly in the video and audio sections. So as to appeal to as many people as possible, cutting across age and cultural differences, Irish/Celtic music has been chosen to illustrate several points, and you will be hearing some Irish music on the video and audio.

1 Musical pattern

Aims   The aims of this section are to enable you to begin to use mathematical ideas to explore musical patterns and to see ways in which these patterns can be represented and better understood. You will also be introduced to sine curves.   ◇

1.1 What sort of tune is this?

Shortly you will be asked to watch the video band *Sounds Harmonious*, which is a central part of this unit. It introduces many of the key themes covered in this and later sections, and also helps to familiarize you with some of the musical terms that are used.

A 'session' is a musical event, where people bring along instruments and play together.

In the first part of the video band you will hear a selection of Irish/Celtic *session* tunes. Do take the time simply to enjoy the music. You will be shown some simple rhythmic and melodic patterns: for instance, you will listen to three types of tune—jig, reel and waltz—and will consider what makes a jig a jig, what makes a reel a reel, and a waltz a waltz.

The second part of the video band takes a more scientific approach to what constitutes a musical note. Here you will see how the pitch of a note is linked to the frequency of a vibration; this is demonstrated by means of an oscilloscope and by computer animations.

As you watch the video, you should note down the main points, as well as new terminology, and any aspects that you are unsure about. Also look out for the mathematical ideas that are used (for example, in diagrams and graphs).

Now watch band 7 on DVD00107, Sounds Harmonious.

Activity 1   Video notes

Having watched the video band, summarize the main points in your learning file, drawing on the notes that you made while viewing. Make sure that you include the following elements:

◇   key musical terms, particularly those that were previously unfamiliar to you;

◇   the mathematical ideas that were used;

◇   any points that you were unsure about.

1.2   What is a musical note?

Most traditional musicians play music by ear—that is, they learn tunes from each other or from recordings (CDs, tapes, etc.) and play them without the aid of written music. However, the majority of traditional tunes have been transcribed in written form, and in the video band you saw how musical sounds relate to written notation. You are not expected to be able to read music, and the video band was not designed to teach you how to do so, but it should have helped to give you a sense of how music is written down.

When music is represented in written notation, the two main things a musician needs to know about each note are its *pitch* (how high or low the note should be) and its *duration* (how long the note should last). Therefore, conventional musical notation can be understood mathematically as a form of graph, with pitch measured on the vertical scale and duration measured on the horizontal scale, as you saw in the video.

Activity 2   Twang that ruler

If, as a child, you never twanged a ruler on a school desk or blew across the top of a bottle to make a note, then it is time you did!

(a) Place a ruler so that it partially overhangs a hard surface such as a table or a windowsill. Hold the ruler firmly on the surface and twang the end that is overhanging. Vary the length of the overhang and see how the note is affected. What happens, and why? Summarize the connection between the length of the overhang and the pitch of the note obtained.

(b) Find an empty bottle and blow across the open top of it to produce a note. Pour water into the bottle until it is about a quarter full, and blow again. Repeat this procedure for different amounts of water in the bottle, and see how the note varies accordingly. Why does this happen? Summarize the connection between the volume of air in the bottle and the pitch of the note.

An important principle emerges from these simple experiments, namely that the pitch of a note is closely bound up with the frequency of vibration. In fact, when you hear a note, your ear is detecting vibrations in the air. It is the *frequency* of those vibrations that determines the pitch of the note you hear. Whereas musicians denote pitch by means of letters like C, F, G and so on, a more accurate measure of pitch is that favoured by scientists: they use the frequency of vibration to define the note.

Frequencies are normally measured in hertz (Hz), where 1 hertz = 1 cycle per second. The note that musicians call *middle C* has a frequency of 256 Hz; this means that if, when you twanged your ruler, it had produced the note of middle C, then the overhanging part of the ruler would have been vibrating up and down 256 times every second. The C above

The unit of frequency is named after Heinrich Hertz, a German physicist, who died in 1894 at the age of only 37 years.

An oscilloscope generates traces from the sound vibrations in the air.

middle C has a frequency which is double that of middle C, i.e. 512 Hz. These frequencies (256, 512 and so on) can be linked directly to the wave patterns in the traces that are made on an *oscilloscope* by the corresponding notes. For instance, Figure 1 shows the patterns of the traces obtained on an oscilloscope when two tuning forks designed to vibrate at frequency 256 Hz (middle C) and 384 Hz (the note G above middle C), respectively, are struck. As you can see, the curve corresponding to the higher note, G, is more 'bunched up', reflecting the fact that the vibrations are more frequent.

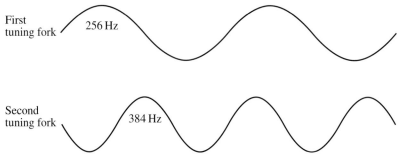

Figure 1   Patterns of oscilloscope traces produced by two tuning forks of different pitches.

In the video you saw oscilloscope traces generated by the sounds from tuning forks and various musical instruments. Such traces are used in developing modern electronic synthesizers which are designed to mimic the sounds of familiar instruments (accordion, cello, fiddle and so on)—the oscilloscope traces from the instruments provide designers with useful models against which to check their electronic versions.

Violins and fiddles are the same instrument distinguished only by the manner of playing and the type of music with which they are associated.

Figure 2 reproduces the oscilloscope traces made by a tuning fork and a fiddle, both sounding at the same pitch, middle C. The frequencies of the traces are the same, which is to be expected as both instruments are producing notes of the same pitch. However, the trace corresponding to the tuning fork is a perfectly smooth wave, which is a feature of the pure sound of this instrument, whereas the trace for the fiddle is 'rougher', though the underlying repeating wave pattern is still evident.

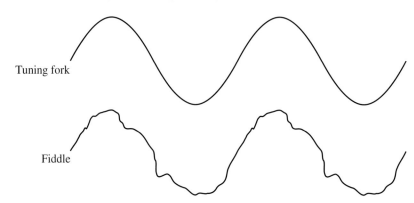

Figure 2   Oscilloscope traces produced by a tuning fork (above) and a fiddle (below), both sounding middle C.

More generally, the trace for every musical instrument has its own characteristic shape, but for simplicity the focus here is on the curve produced by the tuning fork. This regularly repeating smooth wave is called a *sine curve*. In the next subsection you will explore what a sine curve is: you will be asked to use your calculator to look at particular examples of sine curves and other wave curves so as to identify what they have in common and in what ways they differ from one another.

1.3 Investigating sine curves

You may have come across the sine of an *angle* at some time, particularly in relation to angles in triangles. So what is the connection between the trace produced on an oscilloscope by a tuning fork and the sine of an angle?

Before answering this question, it would be useful to give some thought to how angles are measured. You will be familiar with the basic unit of measurement for an angle, which is called a *degree*. There are 360 degrees (written as 360°) in a full turn, and therefore 90° in a quarter turn or right angle. However, there is something rather unsatisfactory about this choice of unit—that is the arbitrariness of the number 360 (why not 10 or 100 or 400, or anything else?).

In mathematics, there is an alternative unit of measurement for angles, which is based solely on the properties of a circle and so does not involve introducing some arbitrary number. This is how the idea of the unit known as the *radian* came about.

Consider a circle with a radius of length r. Suppose two points are marked on the circumference of the circle such that the distance between them around the circumference is equal to r, i.e. the length of the arc is equal to the radius. If these two points are joined to the centre of the circle, an angle is formed as shown in Figure 3. No matter what value the radius r has, the angle formed will always be the same size, and this angle is

It is thought that the choice of 360 subdivisions was first used by the mathematician and astronomer Hipparchus of Nicea (ca. 180 – 125 B.C.), who connected this measure of angle to an earlier attempt by Babylonian astronomers to subdivide the day into 360 parts.

Recall the ribbon on the bodhrán in the video.

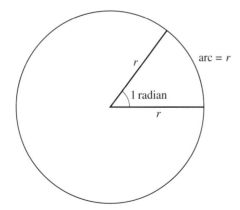

Figure 3 Defining a radian: the arc is equal in length to the radius.

defined as one radian. In other words, the angle subtended at the centre of a circle by an arc equal in length to the radius is defined as one radian. Thus, if the length of an arc is equal to twice the radius, then the angle at the centre is two radians.

In general, as Figure 4 indicates,

$$\text{angle in radians} = \frac{\text{length of arc}}{\text{radius}}.$$

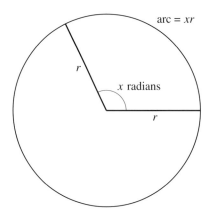

Figure 4   Measuring in radians: the angle in radians, $x = $ arc length/radius.

The radian unit is clearly much larger than the degree—there are approximately 57 degrees in one radian. An exact calculation of the relationship between degrees and radians is set out below.

A well-known property of a circle is that the length of the circumference is 2π times the radius, or $2\pi r$.

Since

$$\text{angle in radians} = \frac{\text{length of arc}}{\text{radius}},$$

it follows that for a full turn of $360°$,

$$\text{angle in radians} = \frac{2\pi r}{r}$$
$$= 2\pi.$$

So,

$$2\pi \text{ radians} = 360°$$

and

$$1 \text{ radian } = \frac{360°}{2\pi}$$
$$= 57.29577951°, \text{ or approximately } 57.3°.$$

One further point is worth noting about the relationship between radians and degrees. As an angle turns through 360°, there are some key points on the way, namely 90° (a quarter turn), 180° (a half turn) and 270° (a three-quarter turn). These fractions of a turn are important when using radians, and they are set out in Table 1.

Table 1

Turns	Degrees	Radians
0	0	0
$\frac{1}{4}$	90	$\frac{\pi}{2}$
$\frac{1}{2}$	180	π
$\frac{3}{4}$	270	$\frac{3\pi}{2}$
1	360	2π

It is particularly helpful to remember that a half turn is π radians and a full turn is 2π radians.

Now return to thinking about sine curves, which are the main focus of this section. In earlier units you have seen graphs showing a pattern between two quantities (with the two quantities corresponding to the labels on the two axes of the graph). It is pertinent here to consider which two quantities are being related in a sine curve such as that produced by the tuning fork in Figure 2. As you saw in the video, the vertical scale for the sine curve in the oscilloscope trace corresponding to the tuning fork represents the *gap* or distance between the tines (or prongs) of the tuning fork (thus a peak in the curve corresponds to when the tines are furthest apart, while a trough is when they are closest together), and the horizontal scale measures *time*.

However, a sine curve is usually drawn with other quantities on the axes: in many mathematical contexts, the horizontal scale shows *angle*, while the vertical scale gives the value of the *sine function* that corresponds to the angle.

To help make sense of where the sine curve comes from, a useful mental image is the circle diagram introduced in the video. The ideas presented there are summarized below. Figures 5 and 6 show a unit circle, i.e. a circle with a radius of 1 unit. Imagine a point P travelling around the circumference of the circle. It starts off at position A and moves anti-clockwise. Throughout, P is connected to the centre, O, by the radius PO. Think about what is happening from two different viewpoints: first, in terms of the *angle* that PO has turned through relative to the horizontal axis (see Figure 5), and secondly, by focusing on the *height* that P is above or below the horizontal axis (see Figure 6).

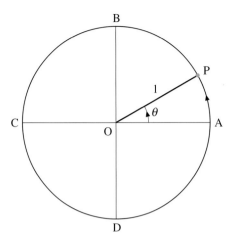

Figure 5 A point P moving around a unit circle,
with the position of *P* given by the angle θ.

In the first case (Figure 5), as P travels around the circle, the angle θ that
the line PO makes with the horizontal axis increases. Starting at A, the
angle θ is zero. When P gets to the top of the circle at B, θ has become a
right angle (90° or $\frac{\pi}{2}$ radians). When P reaches the horizontal axis again,
at C, the angle has become the straight line AOC, corresponding to 180°
or π radians. When P is at the bottom of the circle, at D, θ is 270° or $\frac{3\pi}{2}$
radians. Finally, when P completes the circle and returns to A, it has
made a full turn of 360° or 2π radians. This journey around the circle
represents one full *cycle*. Subsequently, P can continue to travel around
the circle, repeating this pattern over and over. Now re-run the same
scenario in your mind; this time focus not on the angle θ but on the height
of P above or below the horizontal axis. Let that height be called s. This
is shown in Figure 6.

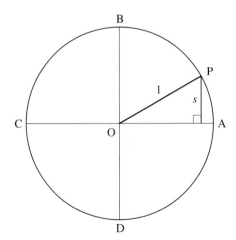

Figure 6 A point P moving around a unit circle, with
the position of P given by the height, s, of P relative
to the horizontal axis.

If P starts at A, the height s is zero (because A lies *on* the axis). As P moves anti-clockwise towards B, s increases quite quickly at first but then more slowly as P nears the top of the circle. At point B, s reaches its maximum value of 1 (remember that this is a *unit* circle). Between points B and C, s reduces to zero—slowly at first and then more quickly. After leaving C, P falls below the horizontal axis, so the height s becomes negative. When P is at the bottom of the circle, at D, s reaches its minimum value of $^-1$. Finally, when P completes the circle and returns to A, s returns to zero. As before, P can continue to travel around the circle, repeating this pattern over and over.

Next put these two scenarios together so that, as P follows its circular path, both the angle θ and the corresponding height s are recorded. Figure 7 shows two specific examples of how θ and s vary under these circumstances.

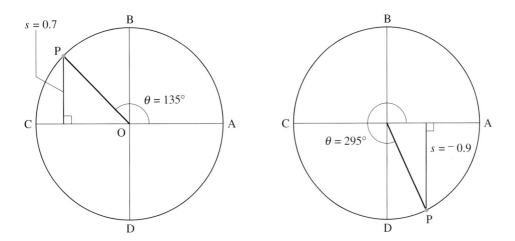

Figure 7   Two examples showing how θ and s vary as P travels round a unit circle.

Table 2 gives a wider range of corresponding values of θ and s.

Table 2

Position of P	At A	Between A and B	At B	Between B and C	At C	Between C and D	At D	Between D and A	At A
Angle θ	0°	30°	90°	135°	180°	220°	270°	295°	360°
Approx. height, s	0	.5	1	.7	0	$^-$.6	$^-1$	$^-$.9	0

These data can be plotted on a line graph, with s on the vertical axis and θ on the horizontal axis. The resulting graph traced on the calculator is shown in Figure 8.

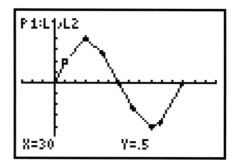

Figure 8   Graph representing the motion of a point P around a unit circle, plotted using data from Table 2.

As you may recognize from the video band, this graph has the distinctive shape of a sine curve. The reason the curve is not very smooth is that only a small number of the possible values of θ have been used in plotting the graph. Suppose, instead, that the values of θ (and the corresponding accurate values of s) were taken every degree, then a graph like that in Figure 9 would result.

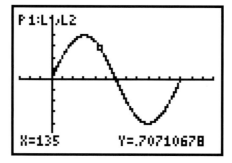

Figure 9   Graph representing the motion of a point P around a unit circle, plotted at degree intervals over the angle range 0° to 360°.

This graph shows one full cycle of a sine curve, and it corresponds to a complete revolution of the point P around the circle. What this means is that the *period* of the sine curve, i.e. the interval between adjacent peaks (or adjacent troughs), corresponds to the point P completing a full turn of the circle. Extend the range of values for θ up to, say, 1000°, and the graph will look like that in Figure 10.

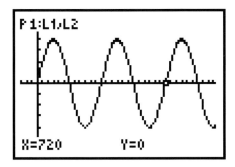

Figure 10   A sine curve representing the motion of a point P over the angle range 0° to 1000°.

As you will see shortly when you come to study Chapter 9 of the *Calculator Book*, a sine curve such as that in Figure 9 or 10 is sometimes referred to as the graph of sin θ. Figure 11 shows two further versions of a sine curve, one with the angles measured in degrees and the other with the angles measured in radians.

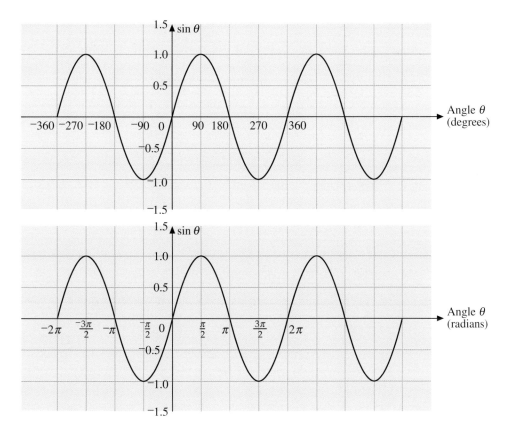

Figure 11   Two sine curves with 'angle' represented on the horizontal axis, one measured in degrees and the other in radians.

In Chapter 9 of the *Calculator Book* you will see how to plot a sine curve for yourself on your calculator. You will also meet two other trigonometric functions—the cosine and tangent functions. Trigonometry is a branch of mathematics that is concerned with relationships between the sides and angles of triangles. However, sines, cosines and tangents also crop up in other areas of mathematics that have little to do with triangles.

Now study Sections 1 and 2 of Chapter 9 in the Calculator Book.

You will meet the trigonometric functions sine, cosine and tangent again later in the course and will use them to model sound and other phenomena. Meanwhile, in the next two sections of *Unit 9*, different mathematical techniques are used to explore patterns in music.

Outcomes

After studying this section you should be able to:

◇   connect the idea of musical pitch to frequency of vibration;

◇   appreciate the units (degrees and radians) used for measuring angles;

◇   recognize easily some of the visual properties of the family of sine curves and use the notion of period;

◇   recognize the graphs of the trigonometric functions sine, cosine and tangent;

◇   predict the likely period of the sum of two sines.

2 Musical scales, intervals and ratios

Aims The aims of this section are to explain the idea of scales in music and to show how the tuning of modern musical instruments is based on the mathematical notion of ratio. ◇

You may recall music lessons in school, where you sang scales using 'doh', 're', 'mi', 'fa', 'soh', 'la', 'ti' to represent the notes. You may not have realized that those notes were, in fact, chosen from twelve possible notes in the required pitch range—these possible notes comprise a 'twelve-note scale'.

2.1 What is a twelve-note scale?

If you play two different notes, the difference in pitch between them is called an *interval*. Certain intervals may sound pleasing to the ear, while others may sound discordant.

On most musical instruments the range of possible intervals is restricted by the number of notes available to be played; for example, a piano has a fixed number of keys, a guitar has a fixed number of *frets*, and so on. Other instruments, such as the fiddle, do not have clearly marked-out notes—there is literally an infinite number of possible notes that could be played on a fiddle, and so you can choose to play any interval you like. For simplicity, this section concentrates on conventional intervals such as might be played on musical instruments with a fixed number of notes, like the piano or guitar.

To explore intervals and the twelve-note scale, start by choosing any note (either white or black) around the middle of the piano keyboard shown in Figure 12. Count this note as number 1 and mentally play consecutive notes (both black and white) going up the keyboard, stopping at note number 13. Now, on a piano the interval between any two adjacent notes, black or white, is a *semitone*—the smallest interval commonly used in Western music. So, as you play the thirteen consecutive notes, you will be going up twelve semitones because there are twelve intervals between the thirteen notes.

Going 'up' the keyboard means moving to the right so as to produce higher notes.

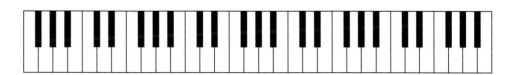

Figure 12 A reduced piano keyboard with 55 notes.

You will see that the sequence of thirteen notes you have played represents a complete cycle based on the repeating pattern of black and white notes on the piano; thus the thirteenth note of this sequence is in the same relative position as the first note, but higher up—in other words, the pattern of black and white notes around it is the same as that around the first note. If you play the first and thirteenth notes on a keyboard, you will find that they sound very similar; the difference is that the thirteenth note is higher in pitch than the first. The interval between the first and thirteenth notes is a particularly important interval; it is called an *octave*, and it is made up of twelve semitones.

In music, a *scale* is the sequence of notes that you might play as you go from the lowest note of a particular octave to the highest note that completes the octave. The scale obtained by playing ALL the possible piano notes in one octave, using both the black and white keys, is an example of what is called a *chromatic scale*.

Chromatic literally means 'coloured'. There is a sense in which the extra notes (over and above the eight that might be expected in a scale) provide extra 'colour' or richness.

The notes in a scale are labelled with letters which are repeated every octave. A chromatic scale therefore has in it twelve differently labelled notes plus a closing note. Each note in a chromatic scale is a semitone apart from its two immediate neighbours. Figure 13 shows how these notes match up to a piano keyboard. The first note in the scale in Figure 13 is labelled C, so this scale is referred to as the chromatic scale *in the key of C*.

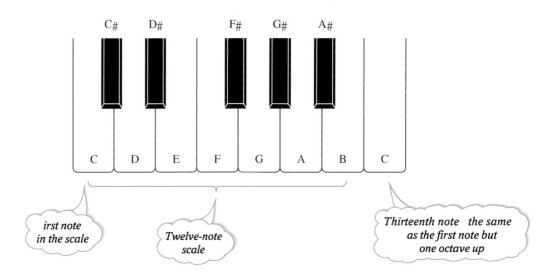

Figure 13 The notes of the chromatic scale in the key of C, marked on a piano keyboard.

A piece of notation that you may be unfamiliar with in Figure 13 is the musical symbol ♯. This is called a *sharp* and has the effect of raising the note it is attached to by one semitone. For example, the note F♯ is one semitone above F. As you can see in Figure 13, on a piano the black notes are the notes with sharps attached. A musical *flat*, written ♭, is commonly used to label notes that are lowered by one semitone, but to keep things simple the 'flat' notation will rarely be used in this unit.

An alternative representation of a chromatic scale makes use of the fact that the names of the notes in a chromatic scale are repeated after each octave, like the hours on a clock face. This cyclical pattern would suggest that some form of circular diagram might be helpful in understanding what is going on. However, because the notes continue to rise after every octave is completed, the preferred representation, shown in Figure 14, is spiral in shape. This diagram stresses the cyclical pattern and the order of the notes.

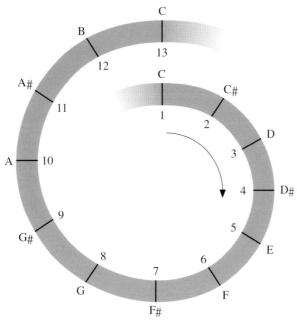

Figure 14   Spiral diagram of a chromatic scale.

Is it twelve notes or thirteen?

Just how many notes there are in a chromatic scale may seem uncertain. The phrases 'the thirteen notes of a chromatic scale' and 'the twelve notes of a chromatic scale' are both used.

There are, in fact, twelve differently labelled notes in such a scale. For example, in the chromatic scale of C, these twelve notes are

C C♯ D D♯ E F F♯ G G♯ A A♯ B.

The thirteenth note, C again, is the first note of a new octave.

Probably the main reason that musicians think of an octave as consisting of thirteen notes is that, when a chromatic scale is played, to stop after the twelfth note leaves a feeling of incompleteness. It is as if you have been left hanging, waiting for the scale to finish. Playing the thirteenth note seems to complete the scale. The main point to remember, however, is that there are twelve semitone intervals in an octave.

If you have access to a musical keyboard, check this for yourself.

2.2 How strange the change from major to minor

Major scales

A chromatic scale uses all the possible notes in an octave, with the notes being equally spaced at intervals of a semitone. Western musicians commonly use other musical scales, such as the major and minor scales, which consist of selections of notes from a chromatic scale. A selection of notes is used because it was found that equal-interval scales, such as chromatic scales, are seldom the best choices musically; instead, scales where the intervals between adjacent notes are not all equal are more pleasant to the ear and are therefore favoured in Western music. Thus, the C *major* scale has eight notes, namely:

C, D, E, F, G, A, B and then back to C.

Adjacent notes in this sequence differ from their neighbours by either one or two semitones, forming a particular pattern that is characteristic of a major scale. On a piano, the C major scale is composed of just the white notes.

> *All major scales have seven uniquely labelled notes; the eighth note, which closes the scale, is the same as the first note but one octave up.*

How are the notes selected for a major scale? To investigate this further in the case of the scale of C major, all the possible notes, i.e. the notes of the chromatic scale in the key of C, are shown numbered from 1 to 13 in Figure 15. The starting note, C, is called the *key note* and is labelled 1. Then the scale of C major consists of the notes labelled

1   3   5   6   8   10   12   13.

> *A* tone *is an interval equal to two semitones.*

This corresponds to the required pattern of tones and semitones for a major scale. From the figure, you can see that these notes are

C   D   E   F   G   A   B   C.

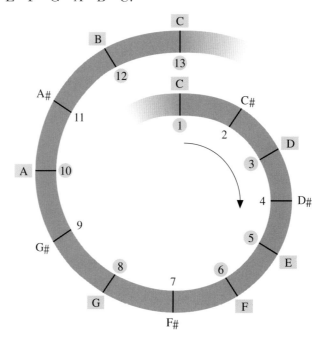

Figure 15   The notes of the scale of C major.

All the major scales conform to the numerical pattern given opposite. So, if the key note is numbered 1, then the relevant notes in the scale can simply be read off as the numerical sequence: 1   3   5   6   8   10   12   13.

Another example is shown in Figure 16. For the scale of G major, the key note is G, which counts as 1, so the scale of G major is

Note number	1	3	5	6	8	10	12	13
Note	G	A	B	C	D	E	F♯	G.

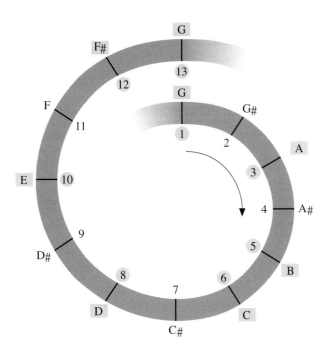

Figure 16   The notes of the scale of G major.

Activity 3   *A major activity*

Using the method described above, write down the notes in the scale of A major.

Minor scales

Minor scales consist of a slightly different selection of notes from a chromatic scale than do major scales. They are associated with a wistful or sad sound and have connections to the notes used in blues music.

Unfortunately, minor scales are harder to define than major scales. For a start, there are at least two commonly used types of minor scale, each with its own pattern of tones and semitones. This is further complicated by the fact that in one type of minor scale the notes used differ slightly depending on whether you are going up the scale or down. To keep things straightforward in this unit, a simplified form of the minor scale will be used. As you will see, this scale is identical to the corresponding major scale, with the exception of the third note which is one semitone lower. For example, the simplified scale of C minor is

Note number	1	3	4	6	8	10	12	13
Note	C	D	D♯	F	G	A	B	C.

The third note is D♯ (usually written in its alternative form as E♭), rather than E as in the scale of C major. This is shown in Figure 17.

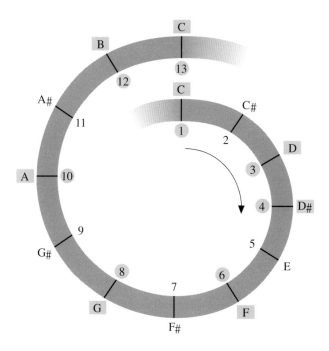

Figure 17   The simplified scale of C minor.

Activity 4   *Minor adjustment*

Write out the notes in the scale of D major and in the simplified scale of D minor.

Different musical scales

There are numerous musical scales that have been used around the world. Almost all cultures understand and use the notion of an octave; however, by no means all choose to divide an octave into twelve semitones. Middle Eastern music, for example, uses quartertones as the smallest musical unit rather than semitones, and there are over three hundred different scales in use. Quartertones are also used in Indian music, and some European composers have written music with even smaller intervals (called *microtones*).

A quartertone is an interval equal to half a semitone.

Another common scale is the *pentatonic scale*, so called because it consists of five notes. An example of a pentatonic scale is provided by the following sequence of consecutive black notes on a piano: F♯ G♯ A♯ C♯ and D♯. Many traditional folk songs are written using pentatonic scales; examples include, 'I Can Wash my Daddy's Shirt', 'Auld Lang Syne' and 'The Skye Boat Song'.

2.3   What is a musical interval?

As was mentioned in Section 2.1, the term *interval* refers to the difference in pitch between two notes—it specifies how far apart the two notes are, i.e. their pitch 'distance'. After listening to two notes played one after another, many people can judge which is higher and which is lower, but they find it more difficult to say how far apart the notes are. The concept of intervals makes this easier.

Intervals

A musical *interval* is a measure of the difference in pitch between two notes. The usual names given to musical intervals are *second*, *third*, *fourth*, *fifth*, *sixth*, *seventh* and *octave*. Sometimes there are higher intervals like *ninth* or *eleventh* (for example, the jazz pianist Fats Waller's hand was said to span an interval of a twelfth). It can be somewhat confusing because some of these words are also used in mathematics for describing the order of things in a list, and for naming fractions. Their use in specifying musical intervals is quite different.

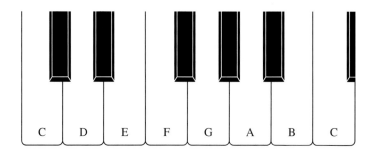

Figure 18   What is the interval between C and G?

Note that musicians speak of the width of an interval, rather than its length.

If you take the notes 'middle C' and 'G above middle C' on a piano (see Figure 18), how far apart are they? In other words, how wide is the musical interval between them? One way of measuring a musical interval is to choose some standard interval as the basic unit or 'step', and to count how many of these steps are required to get from C to G. The obvious step size to choose is the semitone. When counted in semitones, the interval between the notes C and G is found to be seven semitones (see Figure 19). (Remember that consecutive notes on a piano are all one semitone apart.)

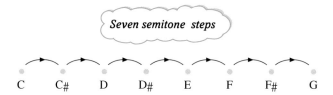

Figure 19   An interval of seven semitones between C and G.

Another way of determining the size of a musical interval is to count using the notes of a particular scale. The scale chosen for this purpose is the scale (usually the major) that starts with the first note of the interval concerned and also contains the second note of that interval. With this method, it is the notes that are counted rather than the gaps between them. In the case of the interval between C and G already considered, G lies in the scale of C major, so count the number of notes in the scale of C major, starting with C. This gives C, D, E, F, G. As G is the fifth note in this sequence, G is referred to as being a (musical) *fifth* above C (see Figure 20).

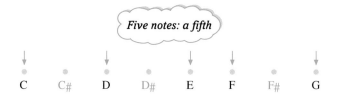

Figure 20   An interval of a fifth in the key of C major.

Likewise, E is a musical *third* above C, F is a musical *fourth* above C, and so on.

Intervals can go down as well as up. So, because C is the fifth note in the *downward* scale of G, C is a musical fifth below G.

You can now try measuring an interval for yourself.

Activity 5   *Measuring intervals*

What is the interval from D up to G?

(a) In semitones.

(b) In musical interval language.

To talk about the interval between two notes—say, between D and G—is actually rather ambiguous, because both the first and last notes in a major scale have the same name, so there are two identically named but different reference points. Therefore, the interval between D and G can be described as either a fifth or a fourth, depending on which note is above the other. Accordingly, a more accurate statement about the interval between D and G would be either that G is a fourth *above* D, or that D is a fifth *above* G.

As you have seen, the term 'interval' in music is used to express how far apart the pitches of two notes are. Now, a useful mathematical model for representing a musical note is a length (thought of as the string of a musical instrument). The interval between two different notes can then be measured mathematically by comparing the lengths of the strings that produce the notes and expressing this comparison as a *ratio*. This model is explored in the next subsection.

Activity 6   *Ratio revision*

Before moving on to use ratios in the context of music, it is worth thinking about where you have met ratios before and briefly reviewing the main points about them in order to check your understanding.

To help, there is a blue-coloured Activity Sheet entitled 'Ratio revision', which lists some of the work that you have done previously, with a reminder of where it was in the course. Consider each topic and jot down what you remember about it. Comment on how confident you feel about your previous understanding and what, if anything, you need to do to improve your grasp of the topic. For example, if you feel very confident about a particular item, you may not need to do anything further. If you feel unsure, you may wish to return to the relevant unit and review the topic. It may also be helpful to look at your notes and the other blue-coloured Activity Sheets covering some of these topics.

2.4 How are intervals represented by ratios?

Strings of musical instruments are usually made from metal wire or plastic, although animal gut was still used for fiddle strings in the early twentieth century.

Musical instruments generate sounds in different ways. In some stringed instruments (for example, a harp or piano) each string makes one fixed note when it vibrates; this is because the effective length of the string cannot be varied. Under these circumstances, the fixed note is essentially determined by the tension in the string. However, the majority of stringed instruments (like the fiddle, the guitar and the sitar) are different: in these, although the basic note produced by a string is determined by setting the string tension (this is what tuning pegs do), the effective length of the string can be altered by the musician's finger pressing the string down on the fingerboard. In this way a single string can produce a number of different notes.

For wind instruments, such as the whistle or flute, sounds are produced when a column of air is vibrated; changing notes involves altering the column length. In certain instruments (like the organ and the *panpipes*) the column lengths are fixed, while in others (like the recorder and the whistle) the length is altered by the musician's fingering.

With stringed instruments, there is a further distinction. The guitar and the sitar are different from the fiddle because they are *fretted*. Whereas a fiddler can make a free choice of how to shorten the length of a string, a guitarist's choices are limited by the positions of the frets (see Figure 21).

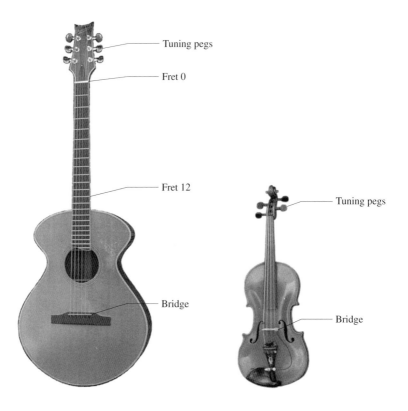

Figure 21   The structure of a guitar and a fiddle.

In the context of stringed instruments a central question is:

What string length is needed to produce a certain note?

This question is examined in the present section. Answering it involves setting up a *mathematical model* that relates the effective length of the string to the pitch of the note that the string produces when it vibrates. The simple model used here stresses the length of the string and ignores other features, such as the tension in the string and the physical material from which the string is made, all of which influence pitch; in other words, this model assumes that these factors are the same for all of the strings being considered.

The key relationships that underpin the model were discovered over two thousand years ago. Western accounts linking mathematics and music look back to Pythagoras, the ancient Greek, who is claimed to have undertaken early investigations into relationships pertaining to sound. Although the truth of legends associating Pythagoras with these relationships is doubtful, the discoveries themselves are valid and striking, and form the basis of the model employed here. The first discovery was that, as you have already seen, the pitch (and frequency) of the note produced by a vibrating string goes up as the length of the string is decreased; correspondingly, the longer the string, the lower the pitch (and frequency) that is produced (this is analogous to the ruler in Activity 2).

The second discovery was that when the string length is halved, the pitch of the note produced is raised by exactly one octave, and the frequency is doubled. This is true irrespective of the length of the original string.

What is of particular significance in these discoveries about pitch is that comparisons are most usefully made using the *ratios* of the string lengths and not the numerical *differences* between the lengths. This distinction exactly parallels one that you have already met in *Unit 2* when making comparisons between prices. There, the distinction was described in terms of a relative comparison (based on the ratio of two prices) or an absolute comparison (based on their numerical difference). The advantage of using relative comparisons is that they apply regardless of the magnitude of the quantities being compared. The same advantage applies here when describing how different string lengths affect pitch.

So, what job is the ratio doing in the present context? The ratio is used here to bring about a multiplicative scaling. In other words, a given quantity is scaled up or down by multiplying by some constant factor—the ratio. When the ratio is less than 1, it produces a scaling down, i.e. a decrease. When the ratio is greater than 1, the effect of the scaling will be to increase the original quantity.

The notion of a mathematical model was first introduced in *Unit 5.*

The Pythagorean approach to tuning, which was commonly used in Western music until the eighteenth century, is explored in Section 3.

You have already come across multiplicative scaling, in *Unit 2* and *Unit 6*. The use of the word 'scaling' here has no connection with the musical scales described in Sections 2.1 and 2.2.

Fractions or dots?

A ratio of one quantity to another is usually written in one of two ways:

- In the form of a fraction; for example, $\frac{3}{4}$ (read either as 'three-quarters' or as 3 over 4.

- In the 'dots' form; for example, 3 : 4 (read as 'the ratio of three to four').

Writing a ratio as a fraction emphasizes that it can be treated as a multiplicative scaling factor; writing it in the 'dots' form emphasizes that it can be seen as a comparison between two quantities.

Only two simple ratios have been mentioned so far in relation to string lengths, namely doubling and halving the string length to produce the note exactly an octave below or an octave above the starting note. However, the same basic principle applies whatever the ratio. For example, rather than halving the string length, suppose you take a string that is three-quarters of the length of the original string and vibrate it. A higher note is produced, but the musical interval between the note produced by the original string and that produced by a string three-quarters its length will be the same whatever the length of the original string. It is simply the *ratio* between the string lengths that determines the musical interval between the notes. For convenience, this ratio is referred to as the *string-length ratio*. It can be found by dividing one string length by the other to produce a fraction; for example, the length of string M, in Figure 22, is $\frac{30}{40} \times$ (length of string L) $= \frac{3}{4} \times$ (length of string L), and so the string-length ratio is $\frac{3}{4}$. In order to simplify the notation, the fraction form of the ratio will be used here rather than the 'dots' form.

Example 1   *String-length ratios and intervals*

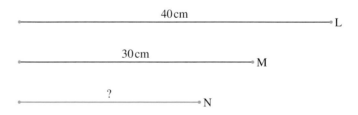

Figure 22   What string length will mean that equal musical intervals are produced?

Figure 22 represents three strings that are different lengths, but otherwise have identical physical properties. String L, which is 40 cm long, is vibrated and a note is produced. Another string (string M), which is 30 cm long, is used to produce a different note. What new length of string (string N) is needed to ensure that the musical interval between the notes from strings M and N is the same as the interval between the notes from strings L and M?

The ratio of the length of string M to the length of string L $= \frac{30}{40} = \frac{3}{4}$. Therefore,

length of string M $= \frac{3}{4} \times$ (length of string L).

For the two musical intervals, i.e. that between the notes produced by strings M and N and that between the notes from strings L and M, to be the same, the string-length ratio for strings M and N must be the same as that for strings L and M. So the length of string N must be $\frac{3}{4}$ of the length of string M:

length of string N $= \frac{3}{4} \times 30 = 22.5$ cm.

Notice that the numerical *differences* between the lengths of strings L and M, 10 cm, and between M and N, 7.5 cm, are different, but the *ratios* of their lengths are the same. Remember that it is the ratios (or relative differences) that are important in determining the musical intervals.

Activity 7   *Calculating with ratios*

Using the method employed in Example 1, calculate the missing string length that would ensure that the musical interval between the notes produced by strings P and Q is the same as that between the notes produced by strings Q and R.

(a) Length of string P $= 9$ cm
Length of string Q $= 6$ cm
Length of string R $= ?$ cm.

(b) Length of string P $= ?$ cm
Length of string Q $= 20$ cm
Length of string R $= 16$ cm.

To recap, you have now seen three ways of specifying musical intervals. These are in terms of:

(a) the number of semitone steps (Section 2.3);

(b) the number of notes counted relative to a musical scale (Section 2.3);

(c) the ratio of the string lengths that produce the notes defining the interval (Section 2.4).

In Section 2.5, the use of string-length ratios to describe musical intervals will be developed further.

2.5 Notes from strings

The ratio of the string lengths needed to produce notes that are an octave apart has been discussed earlier (a string-length ratio of $\frac{1}{2}$ is needed). Now, consider how other notes within the octave are related to string length. Suppose you have a string that gives a particular note, middle C, say, and a string half its length, that gives the C an octave above. What note will be produced by a string that has a length midway between the two? Is it the note that is in the middle of the octave?

These questions are most easily explored by concentrating on the intervals between the notes, rather than on the notes themselves, because, as you have seen, the musical interval between two notes can be represented by the string-length ratio.

Since only relative string lengths are involved, there is no need to use actual lengths; instead, to keep things simple, choose an initial string of length 1 unit. The other two strings being considered here will then be of length $\frac{1}{2}$ unit (producing the note an octave above) and $\frac{3}{4}$ unit (the string midway between the other two in length).

Example 2   A mid-length string

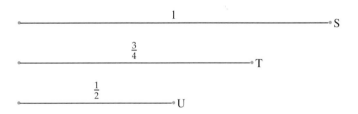

Figure 23   Three strings of lengths 1, $\frac{3}{4}$ and $\frac{1}{2}$.

What are the string-length ratios specifying the musical intervals between the notes produced by the three strings S, T and U shown in Figure 23?

The interval between the notes produced by string S and string T is given by the string-length ratio:

$$\frac{\text{length of string T}}{\text{length of string S}} = \frac{\frac{3}{4}}{1} = \frac{3}{4}.$$

So this musical interval is specified by the string-length ratio $\frac{3}{4}$.

Similarly, the interval between the notes produced by string T and string U is given by

$$\frac{\text{length of string U}}{\text{length of string T}} = \frac{\frac{1}{2}}{\frac{3}{4}} = \frac{1}{2} \times \frac{4}{3} = \frac{2}{3}.$$

So this musical interval is specified by the string-length ratio $\frac{2}{3}$.

Since the two string-length ratios just calculated are not the same, it follows that the musical intervals between the two pairs of notes are not equal. This is summarized in Figure 24.

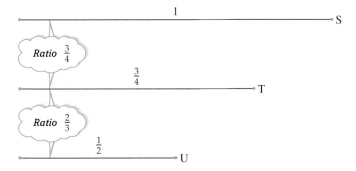

Figure 24   Unequal string-length ratios.

Example 2 demonstrates that although the length of string T is exactly halfway between the lengths of the strings (S and U) that produce notes an octave apart, the note from string T is not halfway through the octave. Consequently, dividing the difference in the string lengths in half does not divide the musical interval into two equal intervals.

Example 3   *Halving an octave*

What length of string produces a note that divides an octave in half, i.e. into *two equal musical intervals*?

Label the strings that produce the notes which are an octave apart as string S and string U, and the string whose note lies in the middle of the octave concerned, as string X. Take the length of string S to be 1, and the length of string U to be $\frac{1}{2}$.

You need to find a particular string-length ratio that will convert the length of string S into the length of string X, and then will convert the length of string X into the length of string U (see Figure 25). Call this ratio r.

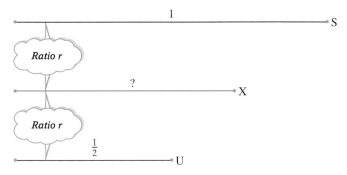

Figure 25   Dividing an octave into two equal intervals.

So,

$$\text{length of string X} = r \times (\text{length of string S})$$

and

$$\text{length of string U} = r \times (\text{length of string X}).$$

It follows that

A substitution is being made here for (length of string X).

$$\begin{aligned}\text{length of string U} &= r \times (r \times \text{length of string S}) \\ &= r^2 \times (\text{length of string S}) \\ &= r^2 \times 1 = r^2.\end{aligned}$$

But the length of string U is $\frac{1}{2}$, so

$$r^2 = \tfrac{1}{2}.$$

Hence,

$$r = \sqrt{\left(\tfrac{1}{2}\right)} = 0.7071067812 \text{ (to 10 d.p.)}.$$

Therefore the length of the string, X, that produces a note which divides an octave into two equal intervals is approximately 0.7071 times the length of string S. As string S is 1 unit long, string X must measure 0.7071 (to four decimal places).

What does this mean in terms of actual notes? Suppose string S in Example 3 produces the note middle C, and string U produces the C an octave above that, i.e. twelve semitones above middle C. Then, the note halfway between these two, which will be six semitones above middle C, will be produced by a string of length $\sqrt{\left(\tfrac{1}{2}\right)}$ times the length of the string that gives middle C. This is shown in Figure 26.

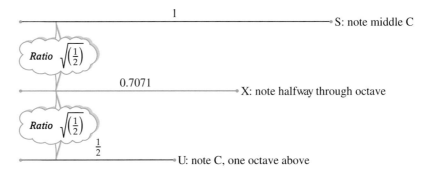

Figure 26   The note halfway through an octave.

From Figure 27, you can see that, in the chromatic scale of C, the note halfway through the octave is F♯.

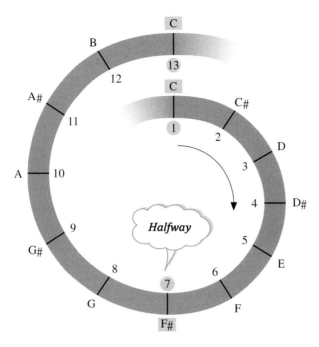

Figure 27   F♯ is the note halfway through the chromatic scale of C.

Of course, this pattern does not only apply to the scale of C. For instance, in the scale of G, to produce the note C♯, which is halfway through the octave (see Figure 28), you need a string of length $\sqrt{\left(\frac{1}{2}\right)}$ times the length of the string that gives the note G.

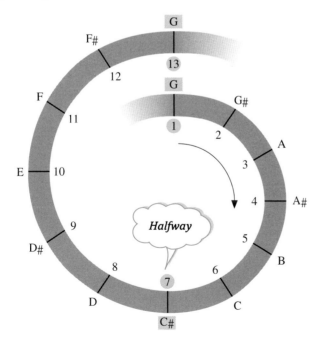

Figure 28   C♯ is the note halfway through the chromatic scale of G.

The same pattern applies to other scales.

Activity 8   *Dividing an octave into three*

In Example 3 an octave was divided into two equal musical intervals, each six semitones wide. In a similar way, an octave can be divided into three equal intervals, each four semitones wide (see Figure 29).

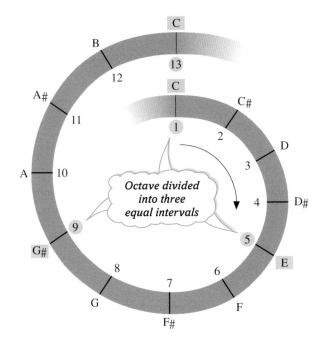

Figure 29   Dividing the octave in the scale of C into three equal intervals.

Use a method similar to that in Example 3 to do the following.

(a) Find an algebraic expression for the string-length ratio, r, for each of these intervals.

(b) Find the value of r, correct to four decimal places.

Calculating roots was dealt with in Sections 4 and 7 of Chapter 1 of the *Calculator Book*.

(c) Calculate the two string lengths that will produce notes which divide an octave into three equal intervals.

Notice the mathematical pattern emerging for the string-length ratios:

To divide an octave into 2 equal intervals, each $\frac{12}{2} = 6$ semitones wide, the string-length ratio, r, must satisfy

$$r^2 = \tfrac{1}{2}.$$

So,

$$r = \sqrt{\left(\tfrac{1}{2}\right)}.$$

To divide an octave into 3 equal intervals, each $\frac{12}{3} = 4$ semitones wide, the string-length ratio, r, must satisfy

$$r^3 = \tfrac{1}{2}.$$

So,

$$r = \sqrt[3]{\left(\tfrac{1}{2}\right)}.$$

What does this pattern lead you to expect for dividing an octave into 4 equal intervals, each $\frac{12}{4} = 3$ semitones wide?

In Activity 8 the lengths of the strings used to divide an octave into three equal intervals were 1, r, r^2, r^3. Therefore the lengths of the strings used when an octave is divided into four equal intervals will be 1, r, r^2, r^3, r^4. The last of these, r^4, is the length of the string that concludes the octave. As you know, the length of that string must be $\tfrac{1}{2}$, so $r^4 = \tfrac{1}{2}$. Thus:

To divide an octave into 4 equal intervals, each $\frac{12}{4} = 3$ semitones wide, the string-length ratio, r, must satisfy

$$r^4 = \tfrac{1}{2}.$$

So,

$$r = \sqrt[4]{\left(\tfrac{1}{2}\right)}.$$

Figure 30 shows roughly what the strings needed to produce four equal intervals will look like.

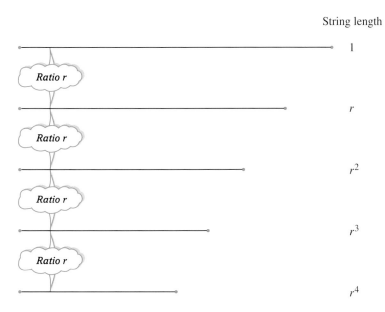

Figure 30   String lengths corresponding to an octave divided into four equal intervals, each three semitones wide.

Notice that dividing the octave into five equal intervals has been omitted. A twelve-semitone interval cannot be divided in this way—5 is not a factor of 12.

A similar argument holds for dividing an octave into six equal intervals, each of two semitones. The lengths of the strings required will be 1, r, r^2, r^3, r^4, r^5, r^6. Since the last of these is the string that produces the note which concludes the octave, it follows that $r^6 = \frac{1}{2}$ and therefore $r = \sqrt[6]{\left(\frac{1}{2}\right)}$.

You will shortly be asked to extend this pattern to calculate the string-length ratio corresponding to the twelve-note scale to which most modern musical instruments are tuned. First, however, it would be a good idea to review the key ideas that you have covered so far in this subsection.

Activity 9 *Stringing it all together*

Complete the table below, which draws on the ideas already dealt with in Section 2.5. Completing the final column of the table will involve using your calculator to find roots.

Number of notes in a given octave	Number of equal intervals in a given octave	Number of semitones in each interval	Value of the string-length ratio, r
3	2		$\sqrt{\left(\frac{1}{2}\right)} =$
4			
5			
7			

Notice from Activity 9 that as the number of notes in the octave increases, the size of the intervals decreases and the string-length ratio gets closer to 1.

You will now explore the question:

What string lengths are needed to produce twelve equal semitone intervals in an octave?

This is the same as asking: 'What is the string-length ratio that produces intervals of a semitone?' Of course, this pattern of intervals in an octave corresponds to a chromatic scale.

Activity 10 *A single semitone*

Details of how to find r using your calculator are covered in Section 9.3 of the Calculator Book (see Section 3 of this Unit).

(a) How many times does the string-length ratio, r, for a semitone need to be applied to a string of length 1 in order to get a string of length $\frac{1}{2}$?

(b) Find an algebraic expression for the ratio r that produces intervals of a semitone, and find r to four decimal places. Explain in your own words what the value of r actually means.

Notice what this activity has shown. An octave can be divided equally into twelve semitone intervals, but the required string-length ratio is quite a complicated decimal. The chromatic scale of notes produced by this method is called an *equally-tempered* scale. The term 'equally-tempered' means, literally, equally-tuned, i.e. the notes are tuned so that they have equal intervals between them.

You will investigate methods of tuning further in Section 3.

Activity 11   *Other equally-tempered intervals*

In this activity, r is the string-length ratio required to produce semitone intervals. As you found in Activity 10, $r = \sqrt[12]{\left(\frac{1}{2}\right)}$.

(a) Earlier you saw that a musical *fifth* is an interval of seven semitones (see Figures 19 and 20). So the string-length ratio needed to produce a fifth is r^7. If a string length of 1 yields a given note, what is the string length that yields the note which is a musical fifth above that note?

Notice that the calculated string length is close to a simple fraction. What is that fraction? This is an important idea that is taken up in Section 3.

(b) An interval of a *fourth* is five semitones wide, so the string-length ratio that produces a fourth is r^5. What is the string length (correct to three decimal places) that produces a note which is a musical fourth above a given note, where the given note is sounded by a string of length 1?

Notice that the string length calculated here is also close to a simple fraction. What is that fraction?

(c) In terms of the string-length ratio for a semitone, r, show that a fourth followed by a fifth (and also a fifth followed by a fourth) is exactly one octave.

Outcomes

After studying this section you should:

◇   be aware of a range of musical terms including 'interval', 'octave', 'scale', 'chromatic scale', 'semitone', 'key', 'major scale', 'minor scale' and 'sharp', as well as the names used for musical notes;

◇   understand the patterns of notes in major and simplified minor scales;

◇   understand three ways in which musical intervals are specified:
    – in semitones,
    – as musical intervals like fourths and fifths,
    – as ratios of string lengths;

◇   be able to calculate, *in general*, the string-length ratio that corresponds to any interval consisting of a simple number of equally-spaced notes in an octave;

◇   be able to calculate, *in particular*, the string-length ratio corresponding to semitone intervals in an octave.

3 Playing in tune

Aims   The aims of this section are to explore an alternative way of tuning musical instruments (called Pythagorean tuning) and to see how it is based on patterns of simple fractions.   ◇

In Section 2 you saw that, for a stringed instrument, the pitch of a note depends on the length of the string that produces the note. Recall that, in general, longer strings give lower notes and that pitch rises by one octave when the string length is halved. You also met the notion of a musical interval and considered what string lengths are required to produce the notes corresponding to various intervals in a given octave. This was investigated for different numbers of equal intervals within the octave, and the relevant string lengths were calculated using a simple ratio—the string-length ratio. The larger the number of notes in the octave, the smaller will be the intervals between them, and the closer to 1 will be the string-length ratio required. The section ended with the application of this principle to the conventional twelve-note scale, which consists of twelve semitone intervals. Here, you should have discovered (in Activity 10) that the string-length ratio which corresponds to an interval of one semitone is $\sqrt[12]{\left(\frac{1}{2}\right)}$ (or approximately 0.9439).

Have a go at Activity 12 next to reinforce your understanding of these ideas.

Activity 12   *Twelve in a row?*

Suppose that you pluck a taut string of length 1 unit. Now take a string that is shorter by a ratio of 0.9439.

(a) How long is the new string?

(b) If the shorter string is plucked, will the resulting note be higher or lower than the note sounded by the original string? Why?

(c) By how many semitones will these two notes differ?

(d) Suppose that eleven further applications of the same string-length ratio are carried out one after the other (making twelve applications of the ratio in all), calculate the length of the final string. If this string is plucked, how will the pitch of the resulting note compare with that produced by the original string of length 1?

3.1   Two forms of tuning

In Western music most modern instruments are tuned using the principle of equally-tempered tuning, which you met in Section 2. Other terms employed to describe this type of tuning are 'well-tempered' and 'equal-temperament'. There is a certain mathematical logic to the equally-tempered approach to tuning instruments, with the semitones all being equally-stepped intervals.

However, until around the time of Johann Sebastian Bach (1685–1750) a system known as *Pythagorean tuning* was used, and most instruments were tuned to slightly different pitches to those common today. As you will see and hear in this section, the Pythagorean approach was built on the (valid) notion that taking simple fractions of string lengths produces very harmonious intervals. For instance, you have already seen that the simplest fraction, a half, produces what is deemed to be the most harmonious interval, an octave. Another simple fraction, two-thirds, also produces a pleasing interval: a musical fifth, which is an interval of seven semitone steps. Provided that tunes were played in the musical key to which the old instruments were tuned, the results of Pythagorean tuning were very harmonious. Problems arose when musicians wished to play in different keys; then the simple fractional relationships between the notes began to break down. As you will hear in the audio band associated with this section, the more distant the key from the one to which the instrument had been tuned, the more painful the results in terms of producing discordant intervals.

Recall Activity 11.

Bach was thrilled with the new 'well-tempered' tuning and revelled in the opportunity to write keyboard pieces for any key—something that musicians take for granted today. In his famous 48 Preludes and Fugues (24 of each) composed for 'the well-tempered clavier', Bach systematically worked through every possible major and minor key (twelve of each).

Clavier is another word for keyboard. When spelt with the letter k, Klavier is German for piano.

Section 3.2 looks more closely at how Pythagorean tuning was organized.

3.2   Pythagorean tuning

As is the case for equally-tempered tuning, the aim of Pythagorean tuning was to create a suitable number of notes within an octave. In terms of string lengths, this meant finding a number of lengths lying between the longest string (say, of length 1) and the string (of length $\frac{1}{2}$) that produced a note an octave higher.

The interval with a string-length ratio of exactly $\frac{2}{3}$ is often called a perfect fifth.

Because musical fifths sound so pleasing to the ear, the Pythagorean approach involved using them repeatedly to determine the notes within the octave. You saw in Activity 11 that a musical fifth corresponds very closely to a string-length ratio of $\frac{2}{3}$. So the simplest form of Pythagorean tuning involves reducing the string lengths repeatedly by a factor of $\frac{2}{3}$, thereby producing a scale of notes that is pleasing to the ear. This procedure is demonstrated opposite.

Bear in mind, as you read through what follows, that the aim of this tuning is to produce notes *within the octave*, i.e. notes that correspond to string lengths between 1 and $\frac{1}{2}$ inclusively. Therefore start with a string of length 1, which gives the lowest note of the octave. Then the string of length $\frac{1}{2}$ produces the highest note of the octave. Next take a string of length $\frac{2}{3}$, which will produce a note that is a musical fifth above the lowest note. So there are now three strings, of lengths $\frac{1}{2}$, $\frac{2}{3}$ and 1, which produce notes that sound harmonious together. A fourth string can be specified that will sound pleasing when played with the other strings. This is done by taking a string length that is $\frac{2}{3}$ of the length of the middle string. Thus the fourth string should measure $\frac{2}{3} \times \frac{2}{3} = \frac{4}{9}$. These four strings are shown in Figure 31.

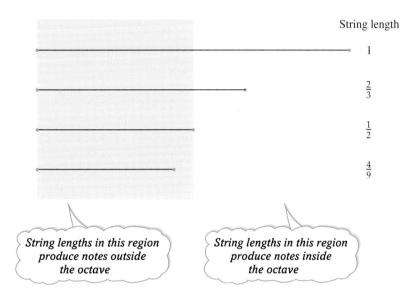

Figure 31   Four string lengths calculated according to Pythagorean tuning.

Unfortunately the fourth string has a length of less than $\frac{1}{2}$, so it is just too short to lie inside the required range of string lengths, i.e. between $\frac{1}{2}$ and 1 inclusively. In terms of musical pitch, this means that the note produced by the string is just too high to be within the given octave—it is in the octave above. However, the equivalent note that is an octave below can be used instead, and this note *will* be in the given octave. Recall that to produce a note that is an octave below another note requires a string twice as long; therefore, the 'replacement' note will be produced by a string that is double the length of the $\frac{4}{9}$ string, and so measures $\frac{8}{9}$. Thus the four string lengths that produce notes within the required octave are $\frac{1}{2}$, $\frac{2}{3}$, $\frac{8}{9}$ and 1, and these are shown in Figure 32 overleaf.

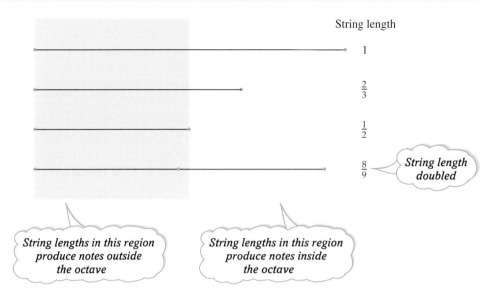

Figure 32   Four string lengths that produce notes within an octave, calculated according to Pythagorean tuning.

The procedure can be continued in this manner—multiply each new string length by $\frac{2}{3}$, and if the result lies outside the required octave range (i.e. the resulting length is numerically less than $\frac{1}{2}$), then simply double the length and get the note that is an octave lower and so is within the range (i.e. the string length is between $\frac{1}{2}$ and 1). If this procedure is continued until six notes have been determined, the final string length will be very near to $\frac{1}{2}$, and the set of notes obtained will be a close approximation to a pentatonic scale. Such scales were described in Section 2.2 as having five notes—here the sixth note completes the scale in the same way as the thirteenth note completes a chromatic scale.

Activity 13   *A Pythagorean pentatonic scale*

Using the method described above, generate a six-note Pythagorean pentatonic scale. Use your calculator to produce the decimals that specify each string length, and copy your results into the table below. Remember that if the calculated string length is less than $\frac{1}{2}$, you will need to adjust the length by doubling it.

Note number	String length	Adjusted string length	Decimal string length (to 2 d.p.)
1	1		1.00
2	$\frac{2}{3}$		0.67
3	$\frac{4}{9}$	$\frac{8}{9}$	
4			
5			
6			

If the bottom note of a scale corresponds to a string length of 1, then the top note, an octave above, should correspond to a string length of $\frac{1}{2}$, i.e. 0.5. As you can see, the string length that you have calculated in Activity 13 for the sixth note in the scale is quite close in value to 0.5 and so, for convenience, can be used to specify the top note. Therefore, this particular selection of six notes provides both a starting point and a finishing point for the octave, as well as a fairly even spread of notes within the octave. These features are typical of a pentatonic scale and explain why it is well recognized and has been used in folk music for centuries.

What would happen if, instead of stopping at the sixth note, the procedure of multiplying successive string lengths by $\frac{2}{3}$ and adjusting if necessary were continued further? When would another string length very close to $\frac{1}{2}$ be generated, along with a good spread of notes within the octave? The next occasion when these features come together is, in fact, for the twelve-note scale, and twelve turns out to be, mathematically, the optimum number of notes for a scale. Section 9.3 of the *Calculator Book* provides an opportunity to investigate this efficiently using a short program. It will also let you review your understanding of the equally-tempered twelve-note scale.

Now work through Section 9.3 of the Calculator Book.

You should be aware that the sequence of decimal numbers you have just generated on your calculator actually corresponds to a *simplified* version of a Pythagorean twelve-note scale. There are basically two flaws in what you have obtained.

Firstly, a guiding principle in producing a Pythagorean scale is that it should be based on *simple* numerical ratios. But the fractions produced by this method get ever more complicated, and the final ones, based on $\left(\frac{2}{3}\right)^{11}$ and $\left(\frac{2}{3}\right)^{12}$, are far from simple! It is possible to improve the scale by replacing the final few complicated fractions with simpler ones based on powers of the fraction $\frac{3}{4}$. In practice, Pythagorean tuning uses a combination of the fractions $\frac{2}{3}$ and $\frac{3}{4}$; exactly how this is done is not explored here.

A second flaw is that the final value, $\frac{262144}{531441}$, has a decimal value of 0.49327, which is close to $\frac{1}{2}$ but not exactly the same. Thus, as with the pentatonic scale, this twelve-note scale does not precisely close on itself.

Activity 14   *Can you tell the difference?*

You can now consolidate your understanding of many of the ideas introduced in this unit so far by listening to Band 4 of CDA5509 (Track 16). In particular, the audio will enable you to hear the musical distinctions explored in the text and to refresh your understanding of them. As you listen, you are advised to note down key ideas and musical terms, as well as any questions that might require further consideration. Topics covered include:

◇   chromatic scales, and major and minor scales;

◇   some simple tunes played using a pentatonic scale (for example, using only the black notes on the piano);

◇   Pythagorean and equally-tempered scales;

◇   transpositions to a different key on an instrument with Pythagorean tuning, and also with equally-tempered tuning—in the first case, with discordant consequences!

Outcomes

After studying this section you should be able to:

◇   understand how Pythagorean tuning uses simple fractions to generate scales;

◇   calculate Pythagorean scales with the aid of your calculator, and compare the notes produced with those in an equally-tempered scale.

4 Consolidation of Block B

Aims   This section aims to help you to revise and consolidate the skills that you have learned in Block B, i.e. in *Units 6, 7, 8* and *9*. The intention is that you should be confident about using the algebraic, graphical and calculator skills from Block B before proceeding to Block C.   ◇

You will soon have completed two of the four blocks of MU120 and you are over halfway through the course. By now you will have developed a wide range of mathematical and calculator skills, as well as communication and study skills. You will need to use and build on these skills in Block C, so now is a good time to take stock. This section therefore revisits the key ideas and skills that you have come across in Block B. As the section has a different purpose, its style differs from that of the previous sections in this unit.

Consider your progress so far and think about which areas you need to concentrate on most. Many students will not have time to do all the activities in this section in detail, so it might be useful to prioritize your revision work before you start.

Activity 15   Review of Block B

Find the blue-coloured Activity Sheet entitled 'Review of Block B', which is designed to help you go over the main ideas, skills and concepts in the block. Look at the topics listed and consider how confident you are about them.

To review your calculator skills, read the summary in Section 9.4 of the *Calculator Book*, omitting the brain stretchers for the moment. Do you need to revise any of the graphing facilities?

Now look back at your work for *Units 6, 7* and *8* and identify the topics where additional practice or consolidation would be beneficial. You might find it useful to glance at the unit outcomes which are set out near the end of each unit.

When you have carried out this review, take a look at the activities in the rest of this section, as well as at the exercises in *Resource Book B* and the brain stretchers in Section 9.4 of the *Calculator Book*, and plan your study accordingly. Initially concentrate on any topics that you are concerned about, and then briefly review the topics that you are more comfortable with. Depending upon the time you have available, you might skim over some parts of the activities/exercises and their solutions if you feel reasonably confident about the topics involved.

The next three subsections should help you to revise the basic ideas in *Units 6, 7* and *8*, respectively.

4.1 Ups and downs

In *Unit 6* you extracted data about the route of a planned walk from maps. You input data into your calculator and plotted profiles of the land traversed. You also used Naismith's rule to estimate the length of time that it would take to walk a planned route, and you employed Pythagoras' theorem to calculate distances. In *Unit 7* you used distance–time graphs to represent journeys, and you interpreted the slopes of graphs. In *Unit 8* you represented problems algebraically, manipulated algebraic expressions and solved equations. Finally, in this unit (*Unit 9*) you have used trigonometric functions. The activities below, whilst based upon the ideas from *Unit 6*, integrate those ideas with the skills developed throughout Block B.

If you find that there are parts of these activities about which you are unsure, then you should revise the relevant sections of the units or *Calculator Book.*

Activity 16 *Planning a walk*

(a) Input into your calculator, as lists, the following data on a proposed walk. Then plot the data points as

(i) a scatterplot,

(ii) a line graph.

Point on walk	Distance from start/ km	Height above sea level/ m
A	0	100
B	10	200
C	15	200
D	20	300
E	25	600

(b) What implicit assumptions are made in the line-graph representation?

(c) Naismith's rule states that the time t hours taken to walk a distance d km, involving ascending a height h m, is given by

$$t = \frac{d}{5} + \frac{h}{600}.$$

Use this rule to estimate the time taken to complete each section of the walk, and so fill in the table opposite.

Point	Distance from start/km	Height above sea level/m	Horizontal distance from previous point/km (d)	Vertical ascent from previous point/m (h)	Time from previous point/hours	Time from start/ hours
A	0	100	0	0	0	0
B	10	200				
C	15	200				
D	20	300				
E	25	600				

(d) On your calculator, plot a distance–time graph for the proposed walk, and use this graph to determine which sections of the walk will have fast walking speeds and which slow ones.

(e) Suppose that you decide to stop for a picnic lunch after you have been walking for 3 hours. Use the distance–time graph that you obtained on your calculator in part (d) to estimate approximately where your lunch stop will be.

(f) Algebra can give you a more precise estimate of the location of the lunch stop. Suppose it is at a point P, which is a distance d km past point B. Now you can use Naismith's rule for the journey from A to P: you know that the time from A to P is 3 hours, so put this value into Naismith's rule and show that the equation is

$$3 = \frac{d + 10}{5} + \frac{100}{600}.$$

(g) Manipulate the equation in (f) so as to make d the subject, and hence find where you would be (according to Naismith's rule) at lunchtime.

(h) There is a direct route from E back to A, which appears, from the map, to be 2 km in horizontal distance. However, it also involves a descent of 500 m. Sketch the profile of this part of the route, and then use Pythagoras' theorem to find the straight-line distance from E back to A. Would you expect the actual distance you would have to walk along this route to be more or less than this straight-line distance?

Activity 17   *Road and map gradients*

A new road is planned to go straight up a steep hill. The distance measured from the bottom of the hill to the top, straight up the hillside, is 1.5 km. The change in height is 250 m.

(a) The road gradient is the change in height divided by the road distance measured along the ground. Find the road gradient of the new road.

(b) The map gradient is the change in height divided by the horizontal distance. Suppose that, for the new road, this horizontal distance is x m. Sketch the profile of the road, and then use Pythagoras' theorem to obtain an equation involving x. Solve the equation to find x. Hence find the map gradient of the road.

(c) Explain why you would expect the map gradient to be greater than the road gradient.

(d) If the angle of inclination of the road to the horizontal is θ, the trigonometric ratios for θ are related to the road and map gradients in the following ways:

$$\sin \theta = \text{road gradient},$$
$$\tan \theta = \text{map gradient}.$$

Use your answer to part (a) to find the angle θ (in degrees) from the formula:

$$\theta = \sin^{-1}(\text{ road gradient}).$$

Then, using the formula $\tan \theta = \text{map gradient}$, check that θ gives the same result for the map gradient as you obtained in part (b).

If you think that you still need more practice with these ideas, do some of the relevant exercises in *Resource Book B*—the exercises in the sections relating to *Units 7* and *8* may be helpful, as well as those in the *Unit 6* section.

4.2   Conversion factors

Recall that in *Unit 7* you met formulas for converting between different units—for example, for converting pints into litres. The formulas were expressed as mathematical functions. You used your calculator to plot the graphs of these functions and employed the trace and table facilities to extract information for converting particular quantities. You also manipulated conversion formulas so as to obtain the *inverse functions*, which could be used to convert in the opposite direction. The relevant algebraic skills were practised in *Unit 8*, but are much more widely applicable. In Block C you will need to be able to plot the graphs of mathematical functions that arise in a number of different contexts and to manipulate those functions algebraically. The next two activities are designed to help you to consolidate your skills in these areas.

As before, some parts of the activities may highlight areas where you need to revise or practise certain skills; if so, then refer back to the relevant sections in the units.

Activity 18   Degrees to radians and back

(a) You saw in Section 1.3 of this unit that 1 radian $= \frac{360}{2\pi}$ degrees. Suppose a particular angle measured in degrees is $D°$, and the same angle measured in radians is R radians. What is the mathematical function that gives D in terms of R?

(b) Change the variables in the function obtained in part (a) to ones that are suitable for inputting the function into your calculator. Input this function as Y1, and plot its graph on the calculator. Use the trace and zoom facilities to convert an angle of 2.6 radians into degrees.

(c) Rather than using the graph as in part (b), substitute into the function directly to convert 2.6 radians into degrees.

(d) Manipulate the function you obtained in part (a) so as to make R the subject.

(e) Your answer to part (d) is the function that gives R in terms of D. Change the variables to ones that are suitable for inputting the function into your calculator. Input the function as Y2, and use it to convert 135° into radians.

(f) Function Y2 converts degrees into radians and so undoes the conversion that function Y1 does. Function Y2 is called the inverse function of function Y1, and vice versa: what one function does, the other undoes. Check that this is so by inputting any value into function Y1 and then inputting your answer into function Y2. Next, input any number into function Y2, and the answer into function Y1. In both cases you should end up with your original number.

(g) Explain why the graphs of both functions are straight lines that pass through the origin. Explain how the gradient of each line can be predicted from the function.

Activity 19   *Temperature conversion*

(a) If a particular temperature measured on the Celsius scale is $A\,°\mathrm{C}$ and measured on the Fahrenheit scale is $B\,°\mathrm{F}$, then A and B are related by the conversion function:

$$A = \frac{5}{9}B - \frac{160}{9}.$$

Input this function into your calculator as Y1, and produce its graph on the calculator screen. Use the function to convert $50\,°\mathrm{F}$ into Celsius.

(b) Substitute $A = 20$ into the function from part (a) to obtain an equation for a temperature $B\,°\mathrm{F}$ which corresponds to a temperature of $20\,°\mathrm{C}$. Solve this equation for B.

(c) Manipulate the equation in part (a) to make B the subject. Input this function into your calculator as Y2. Use this function to convert $10\,°\mathrm{C}$ into Fahrenheit.

(d) Explain why function Y1 and function Y2 are inverse functions.

(e) Explain why the graphs of function Y1 and function Y2 do not pass through the origin. Explain how the gradient and intercept of each graph can be predicted from the function.

If you found that there were parts of these activities that you were unsure about, revise the relevant sections in the units and/or in the *Calculator Book*, and then practise similar exercises in *Resource Book B*.

4.3   Number games

Section 1 of *Unit 8* involved the construction of a formula for a number game by using the instructions for the game. The formula gave the final number obtained in the game, in terms of the input number (the number you first thought of). Algebraic manipulation of the formula enabled you to analyse the game and to explain why it worked.

Such skills are useful in many different situations, some of which you will meet in Block C. In *Resource Book B* (*Unit 8* section) there are several exercises that will give you practice in these important algebraic skills. The next two activities allow you to revise and extend your understanding of these ideas.

Activity 20   Think of a number revisited

Construct a formula for each of the following number games. Simplify the formula and hence explain why the numerical 'conjuring trick' involved works or not, as the case may be. If the 'trick' does not work, suggest an amendment that will make it work.

(a) Think of a number (say, N); double it; add 4; divide by 2; take away the number you first thought of; and the answer is 2.

(b) Think of the year (say, Y) in which you were born; subtract it from 2000; the result is your age in the year 2000.

(c) Think of a number (say, P); subtract it from 20; double the result; add 5; subtract the number you first thought of; divide by 3; add the number you first thought of; and the answer is 15.

(d) Think of a number (say, M); subtract it from 10; multiply the result by 3; add 10; subtract the number you first thought of; divide by 4; subtract the number you first thought of; and the answer is 10.

(e) Think of a positive number (say, X); subtract 1; square the result; add the number you first thought of; subtract 1; add the number you first thought of; take the square root; divide by the number you first thought of; and the answer is 1.

(f) Think of a number (say, Q); add 2; square the result; subtract 4; divide by the number you first thought of; add the number you first thought of; and the answer is 4.

Activity 21   *Think of a number of cans*

(a) The price of a can of beans at a wholesale market is 4 pence, and a shopkeeper buys X cans. Write down the cost, *in pence*, of this purchase to the shopkeeper.

(b) The cost of the transport for the round trip to the wholesale market in order to buy the beans is £10. Write down the total cost, *in pence*, of X cans of beans, including the transport.

(c) The shopkeeper wants to make a profit equal to the total cost (including transport). How much is the total cost plus profit? How much is this equivalent to per can? This must be the selling price, P pence, per can.

(d) Show that the function which gives P in terms of X is

$$P = 8 + \frac{2000}{X}.$$

(e) Plot this function on your calculator and use the trace and/or table facility to find

  (i) the value of P when X is 100,

  (ii) the value of X when P is 10.

  Comment on the implications of your results for the shopkeeper.

(f) Repeat part (e) using algebraic methods instead of a calculator graph.

The above two activities have involved the following:

◇ constructing formulas for particular purposes;

◇ simplifying them by means of algebraic manipulation;

◇ using the calculator to input a function and plot its graph;

◇ solving for one variable by using the trace and table facilities on the calculator or by using algebraic manipulation.

If you found that there were parts of these activities that you were unsure about, revise the appropriate sections in the units or in the *Calculator Book*, and then practise the relevant exercises in *Resource Book B*.

4.4 *Learning and studying skills*

The end of a block is a good time to look back at how you are tackling the course. It is an opportunity to identify the things that you are doing well and the things that you need to work on in the rest of the course.

You may have found this unit a bit more challenging than previous ones because it builds upon earlier work. Many of the remaining units in the course will also build upon work in previous units, so you should try to consolidate your skills regularly. Some parts of the course may seem more difficult than others, and so you may find yourself short of time on occasion, especially if you have plans for other activities during the next few months. If this happens, then consult your tutor and also look at the study advice in the course Stop Presses.

Did the consolidation activities in this section show up places in the block where your study technique could be improved? Jot down points that you think you should take into account in your study of Block C, and bear these in mind as you do Activity 22.

Activity 22 *A skills audit*

Find the cream-coloured Activity Sheet entitled 'Skills audit'. Consider different aspects of your work on MU120 so far: your time management, the way you study the units (specifically, how you do the assignments, the calculator work, the audiovisual work and the written parts of the course) and your use of feedback from your tutor and fellow students (perhaps at tutorials). For all of these aspects, there are no right or wrong answers. You may find some aspects easy and others more difficult. One thing that is often problematic, even for experienced students, is the management of time—keeping up with the demands of the course.

Have a quick look at the skills audit in Activity 4 of *Unit 5*, which was a similar exercise. Has anything changed since then? What do you think are your highest priorities now that you are getting more used to studying mathematics in this way? Finally, pinpoint one or two areas that you think are the most important for you to work on; jot them down, perhaps at the bottom of the Activity Sheet.

Outcomes

Now that you have completed this section, you should be confident that you can:

◇   input data into your calculator, and then plot scatterplots and line graphs;

◇   use Naismith's rule and Pythagoras' theorem to calculate times and distances;

◇   use distance–time graphs to represent journeys, and interpret the slopes of such graphs;

◇   use trigonometric functions and their inverses on your calculator;

◇   represent problems algebraically, manipulate algebraic expressions, and solve equations;

◇   use a conversion function to convert between units;

◇   change the subject of an equation by using algebraic manipulation;

◇   input functions into your calculator, and then plot their graphs on the calculator screen;

◇   explain the relationship between the slope and intercept of a straight-line graph and its equation.

Unit outcomes

After studying this unit you should be able to:

◇   connect the idea of musical pitch to frequency of vibration;

◇   appreciate the units (degrees and radians) used for measuring angles;

◇   recognize some of the visual properties of the family of sine curves and use the notion of period;

◇   recognize the graphs of the trigonometric functions sine, cosine and tangent;

◇   predict the likely period of the sum of two sines;

◇   be aware of a range of musical terms;

◇   understand the patterns of notes in major and simplified minor scales;

◇   understand three ways in which musical intervals are specified:
  – in semitones,
  – as musical intervals like fourths and fifths,
  – as ratios of string lengths;

◇   calculate, *in general*, the string-length ratio that corresponds to any interval consisting of a simple number of equally-spaced notes in an octave;

◇   calculate, *in particular*, the string-length ratio corresponding to semitone intervals in an octave;

◇   understand how Pythagorean tuning uses simple fractions to produce scales;

◇   calculate Pythagorean scales and equally-tempered scales, with the aid of your calculator.

You should also have consolidated your skills in the areas covered by the whole of Block B, especially your algebraic, graphical, calculator, communication and study skills.

Comments on Activities

Activity 1

Every student will have something slightly different here. Many of the key musical terms included in the video can be found in the Musical Glossary at the back of this unit.

The following mathematical ideas were introduced in the video:

- Musical notation has similarities with a pitch–time graph.
- When shortened, a ruler, a column of air or a violin string vibrates with greater frequency and produces a note of higher pitch.
- Repeating rhythmic patterns distinguish different types of tune.
- The note from a vibrating tuning fork produces a sine curve on an oscilloscope.
- The distance between the tines of a vibrating tuning fork, when plotted against time, gives a sine curve.
- For a point travelling around the circumference of a circle, plotting height above or below the diameter against angle at the centre produces a sine curve.
- Angles can be measured in either degrees or radians.

These ideas are developed in the rest of this unit, so if there are points in the video that you are unsure about, they may be clarified as you work through the unit.

Activity 2

(a) You should have found that the note was high when the overhanging length of ruler, which was vibrating, was short.

But why should this be? The explanation lies in the frequency of vibration. From observation, if you twang a long section of ruler, the frequency of its vibrations will be less than if the section were short. It is the vibration frequency that determines the pitch of the note: the more frequent the vibrations, the higher the note.

(b) With the bottle, you should have found that the note was higher when the column of air in the bottle was shorter, i.e. when the bottle was fairly full of water.

A similar principle to that in part (a) applies here. Like short sections of ruler, small columns of air vibrate faster than large ones and so produce higher notes. If you have an opportunity to see a church pipe organ, look at the pipes and consider which pipes make the low notes and which the high notes. Remember the Irish whistle shown in the video and how covering the holes altered the volume of vibrating air, thereby altering the frequency of vibration and hence the pitch of the note.

Activity 3

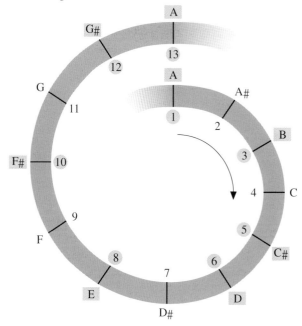

From the above spiral diagram of the chromatic scale in the key of A, the notes in the scale of A major are

1	3	5	6	8	10	12	13
A	B	C♯	D	E	F♯	G♯	A.

Activity 4

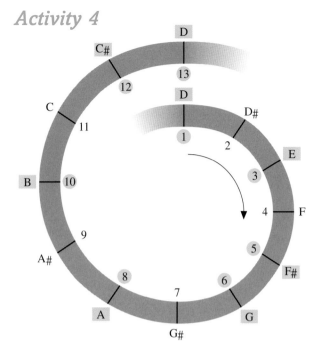

From the above spiral diagram of the chromatic scale, the notes in the scale of D major are

1	3	5	6	8	10	12	13
D	E	F♯	G	A	B	C♯	D.

The notes in the simplified D *minor* scale are the same, except that the third note is lower by one semitone. So, the notes in the simplified D minor scale are

1	3	4	6	8	10	12	13
D	E	F	G	A	B	C♯	D.

Activity 5

(a) Counting the semitone intervals from D up to G can be done like this:

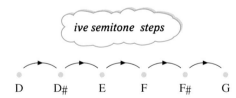

This gives a five-semitone interval.

(b) In musical interval notation, the interval

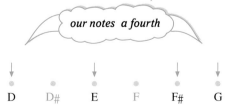

from D up to G can be deduced by looking at the notes that make up the D major scale. In the figure at the bottom of the page, counting D as 1, E as 2, and so on, gives the result that G is a musical fourth above D.

Activity 6

The points listed will differ from person to person, so there are no comments on this activity.

Activity 7

(a) The ratio of the length of string Q to the length of string P $= \frac{6}{9} = \frac{2}{3}$.

So the length of string Q is $\frac{2}{3}$ of the length of string P.

Now, if the musical interval between the notes produced by strings P and Q is the same as that between the notes produced by strings Q and R, then the two string-length ratios must be the same. Therefore, string R must be $\frac{2}{3}$ of the length of string Q. Thus,

length of string R $= \frac{2}{3} \times 6 = 4 \, \text{cm}$.

(b) The ratio of the length of string R to the length of string Q $= \frac{16}{20} = \frac{4}{5}$.

So the length of string R is $\frac{4}{5}$ of the length of string Q.

To maintain the same interval between the notes from strings P and Q as that between the notes from strings Q and R, the two string-length ratios must be the same. Therefore, string Q must also be $\frac{4}{5}$ of the length of string P. Thus,

$\frac{4}{5} \times$ (length of string P) $= 20 \, \text{cm}$.

So,

length of string P $= \frac{5}{4} \times 20 = 25 \, \text{cm}$.

Activity 8

Label the strings needed to produce the notes corresponding to the intervals as S, T, U and V.

(a) The string-length ratio between any string and the next (shorter) one will be the same for all the consecutive pairs of strings because the required intervals must be equal. Call this ratio, r.

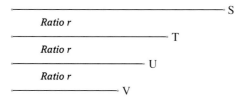

As the octave is being divided into three intervals, three applications of this ratio must convert the length of string S (taken to be 1) into the length of string V (taken to be $\frac{1}{2}$). So,

$$r \times r \times r \times 1 = \frac{1}{2},$$

then

$$r \times r \times r = \frac{1}{2}.$$

(b) From (a),

$$r^3 = \frac{1}{2},$$

therefore

$$r = \sqrt[3]{\left(\frac{1}{2}\right)} = 0.7937.$$

(c) The lengths of strings T and U are calculated by successively applying the string-length ratio r as follows:

length of string T

$$= 0.7937 \times (\text{length of string S})$$
$$= 0.7937 \times 1 = 0.7937 \text{ (to 4 d.p.)},$$

length of string U

$$= 0.7937 \times (\text{length of string T})$$
$$= 0.7937 \times 0.7937 = 0.6300 \text{ (to 4 d.p.)}.$$

Each interval is four semitones wide. This also happens to be the musical interval of a third from a major scale (known as a 'major third'), but the fact that dividing the octave into three produces intervals of thirds is just a potentially confusing coincidence!

Activity 9

The completed table should look like this:

Number of notes in a given octave	Number of equal intervals in a given octave	Number of semitones in each interval	Value of the string-length ratio, r
3	2	6	$\sqrt{\left(\frac{1}{2}\right)} = 0.7071$
4	3	4	$\sqrt[3]{\left(\frac{1}{2}\right)} = 0.7937$
5	4	3	$\sqrt[4]{\left(\frac{1}{2}\right)} = 0.8409$
7	6	2	$\sqrt[6]{\left(\frac{1}{2}\right)} = 0.8909$

Activity 10

(a) To go from one semitone to the next, the string length needs to be reduced by the string-length ratio, r. Since the string lengths (1 and $\frac{1}{2}$) encompass an octave, there are twelve semitones involved, so the ratio needs to be applied twelve times in succession to end up with a string of length $\frac{1}{2}$.

(b) This application of the ratio r can be represented by the equation:

$$r \times r \times r \times r \times r \times r \times r \times r \times r \times r \times r \times r = \frac{1}{2},$$

which can be written as

$$r^{12} = \frac{1}{2}.$$

So,

$$r = \sqrt[12]{\left(\frac{1}{2}\right)} = 0.9439 \text{ (to 4 d.p.)}.$$

This means that for an octave to be divided into twelve equal semitones, a string-length ratio of 0.9439 must be used. This string-length ratio produces the musical interval of a semitone.

Activity 11

(a) The string-length ratio for a *fifth*, r^7, must be applied to the string of length 1. This gives a string length of

$$r^7 \times 1 = \left(\sqrt[12]{\left(\tfrac{1}{2}\right)} \right)^7$$
$$= 0.9438743127^7$$
$$= 0.6674 \text{ (to 4 d.p.)}.$$

This is very close in value to the fraction $\tfrac{2}{3}$.

(b) The string-length ratio for a *fourth*, r^5, must be applied to the string of length 1. This gives a string length of

$$r^5 \times 1 = \left(\sqrt[12]{\left(\tfrac{1}{2}\right)} \right)^5$$
$$= 0.7492 \text{ (to 4 d.p.)}.$$

This is very slightly less than $\tfrac{3}{4}$.

(c) A fourth followed by a fifth would correspond to $r^5 \times r^7$. (Note that as you move from one interval or note to another you *multiply* by the string-length ratio.) Thus,

$$(r \times r \times r \times r \times r) \times (r \times r \times r \times r \times r \times r \times r)$$
$$= r^{12} = \tfrac{1}{2}.$$

Similarly a fifth followed by a fourth corresponds to

$$(r \times r \times r \times r \times r \times r \times r) \times (r \times r \times r \times r \times r)$$
$$= r^{12} = \tfrac{1}{2}.$$

Either way round, the intervals of a fourth and a fifth comprise an octave.

Activity 12

(a) The new string is 0.9439 units in length.

(b) If the shorter string is plucked, it will sound a higher note than that sounded by the original string. This is because shorter strings produce higher notes.

(c) The two notes will differ by one semitone.

(d) The twelve applications of the ratio 0.9439 correspond to a scaling of $(0.9439)^{12}$ or approximately 0.5. The length of the final string will therefore be approximately 0.5.

This string will sound a note approximately one octave higher than that from the original string, because halving the string length increases the pitch by one octave.

Activity 13

The completed table should look like this:

Note number	String length	Adjusted string length	Decimal string length (to 2 d.p.)
1	1		1.00
2	$\tfrac{2}{3}$		0.67
3	$\tfrac{4}{9}$	$\tfrac{8}{9}$	0.89
4	$\tfrac{16}{27}$		0.59
5	$\tfrac{32}{81}$	$\tfrac{64}{81}$	0.79
6	$\tfrac{128}{243}$		0.53

As can be seen from the table, the method of Pythagorean tuning produces a selection of six notes that are reasonably spaced and finish close to the end point of the octave.

Activity 14

While you listened to the audio you should have summarized the key points and also noted any aspects that you found confusing or difficult. If, on reflection, you are still uncertain about anything, replay the appropriate sections of the audio band.

Activity 15

As the outcomes of the review will differ from person to person, there are no comments on this activity.

Activity 16

(a) To plot the data points as a scatterplot and as a line graph (see *Calculator Book*, Section 5.6), put 'Distance from start' along the horizontal axis and 'Height above sea level' along the vertical axis.

(i)

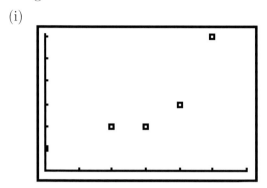

(ii)

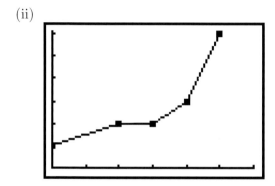

(b) In the line-graph representation, the calculator connects the data points by means of straight-line segments in the order in which the points appear in the lists. The implicit assumptions are that the height of the ground changes *smoothly* and *linearly* between each pair of data points and that the gradient changes *abruptly* at each data point (see *Unit 6*, Sections 2.3 and 4.1). In fact there is no information about the height of the ground anywhere along the walk except at the five data points—it is unlikely that in reality the profile of the land changes in the way assumed. When drawing profiles of the land by hand, it is usual to connect the data points by a smooth curve in order to try to give a more realistic picture of the shape of the ground, although smoothness is itself an implicit assumption.

(Note also that the calculator's line-graph representation of the profile may make the slopes appear very much steeper than they are in reality, since the scales on the two axes are different (see *Unit 6*, Section 4.1).)

(c) By using Naismith's rule (with the estimated times taken to three decimal places) you should obtain the following table:

Point	Distance from start/km	Height above sea level/m	Horizontal distance from previous point/km (d)
A	0	100	0
B	10	200	10
C	15	200	5
D	20	300	5
E	25	600	5

Point	Vertical ascent from previous point/m (h)	Time from previous point/hours	Time from start /hours
A	0	0	0
B	100	2.167	2.167
C	0	1.000	3.167
D	100	1.167	4.333
E	300	1.500	5.833

If you wish, you can check your result for the estimated time for the whole walk (i.e. the time to reach E) by applying Naismith's rule to the total horizontal distance (25 km) and the total vertical ascent (500 m): this gives an estimated total time of $\left(\frac{25}{5} + \frac{500}{600}\right)$ = 5.833 hours (to 3 d.p.), agreeing with the cumulative estimated total time in the table.

Note that the use of Naismith's rule here, both for the individual sections of the walk and for the entire walk, assumes that there are no intermediate descents, as these would change the total of the height ascended (see *Unit 6*, Section 3.3 for an illustration of this).

(d) To plot a distance–time graph for the walk, you should plot 'Time from start' along the horizontal axis and 'Distance from start' along the vertical axis (see *Calculator Book*, Section 7.1; *Unit 7*, Section 2.1).

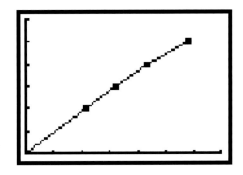

The average walking speed over a section of the walk is represented by the gradient of the corresponding straight line on the distance–time graph (see *Unit 7*, Section 2.1). The steeper the gradient of the graph, the faster the walking speed. You can see that there is not much change in the gradient of the graph over the first three sections of the walk, although over the section CD it is less steep. However, for the last section, DE, the gradient of the graph is less steep, implying that the walking speed is rather slower there. You can calculate these gradients using the data from either the table or the trace facility on your calculator (see *Calculator Book*, Section 6.1).

Section of walk	Average walking speed /km per hour (to 1 d.p.)
AB	4.6
BC	5.0
CD	4.3
DE	3.3

(e) From the distance–time graph that you obtained in part (d), you can see that three hours after starting the walk, you would expect to be somewhere between points B and C. By using the cursor keys to move the cross around the screen (see *Calculator Book*, Section 6.1) you can find that on the straight-line section the point which has X-coordinate 3, has a Y-coordinate of approximately 14, indicating that this point on the walk is about 14 km from the start—about 4 km along the section BC.

You could find the Y-coordinate of this point with greater accuracy by means of repeated use of the Zoom In or ZBox facilities; this would give 14.17 km (see *Calculator Book*, Section 8.5).

(f) If P is at a distance d km from B, it is at a distance $(d + 10)$ km from the start of the walk at A. When P is reached, the total vertical ascent since the start is just the 100 m climb between A and B, since there is no change in height between B and C. Thus, since the point P is reached in a time of 3 hours, the equation given by Naismith's rule is

$$3 = \frac{d + 10}{5} + \frac{100}{600}.$$

(g) Reduce the second fraction on the right-hand side of the equation in (f) to lowest terms:

$$3 = \frac{d + 10}{5} + \frac{1}{6}.$$

Now follow the procedure outlined in the box in Section 4.1 of *Unit 8* to make d the subject of the equation:

subtract $\frac{1}{6}$ from both sides $\qquad \dfrac{17}{6} = \dfrac{d + 10}{5}$

multiply both sides by 5 $\qquad \dfrac{85}{6} = d + 10$

subtract 10 from both sides $\qquad \dfrac{25}{6} = d.$

So, $d = 4.17$ km (to 2 d.p.). Therefore, at lunchtime you can expect to be about 4.17 km (to 2 d.p.) from B, on the way to C.

(h) Your sketch of the profile of the route from E back to A should resemble the figure below.

Change 500 m to 0.5 km so that the units are the same. Let the straight-line distance from E to A be x km. By applying

Pythagoras' theorem to the profile (see *Unit 6*, Section 4.2), you get

$$x^2 = 2^2 + (0.5)^2$$
$$= 4.25.$$

So,

$$x = \sqrt{(4.25)} = 2.06 \text{ (to 2 d.p.)}.$$

Therefore, the straight-line distance from E back to A is about 2.06 km. The actual distance you would have to walk along this route will be more than this, because the path is unlikely to be exactly a straight line—the shortest possible route; it may deviate in both the horizontal (left/right) and vertical (up/down) directions.

Activity 17

(a) Road gradient $= \dfrac{\text{change in height}}{\text{road distance}}$

(see *Unit 6*, Section 4.2). So, in this case, working in metres:

$$\text{road gradient} = \frac{250}{1500}$$
$$= \frac{1}{6} = 0.167 \text{ (to 3 d.p.)}.$$

(b) Your sketch of the profile of the road should resemble the figure below.

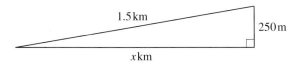

1.5 km

250 m

x km

Pythagoras' theorem applied to the profile gives

$$x^2 + 250^2 = 1500^2.$$

Then,

$$x^2 = 1500^2 - 250^2$$
$$= 2187500.$$

So,

$$x = \sqrt{(2187500)} = 1479$$

(to the nearest integer).

Thus the horizontal distance of the new road is 1479 m (to the nearest metre).

Now,

$$\text{map gradient} = \frac{\text{change in height}}{\text{horizontal distance}}$$
$$= \frac{250}{1479}$$
$$= 0.169 \text{ (to 3 d.p.)}.$$

(c) The distance along the road is represented by the hypotenuse of the right-angled triangle in part (b). As the hypotenuse is longer than the triangle's horizontal side (which represents the horizontal distance), dividing the change in height by the horizontal distance will always give a larger result than dividing it by the road distance. Note that the greater the angle of inclination of the road to the horizontal, the more pronounced will be the difference between the road and map gradients.

(d) From part (a),

$$\text{road gradient} = 1/6.$$

As $\theta = \sin^{-1}(\text{road gradient})$, it follows that

$$\theta = \sin^{-1}(1/6) = 9.594° \text{ (to 3 d.p.)}.$$

Now,

$$\text{map gradient} = \tan\theta$$
$$= \tan(9.594°) = 0.169$$
$$\text{(to 3 d.p.)},$$

which agrees with the answer in part (b).

Note that if you used radians rather than degrees, $\theta = 0.1674480792$ (to 10 d.p) and $\tan\theta = 0.169$ (to 3 d.p.).

Activity 18

(a) Since 1 radian is $\dfrac{360}{2\pi} = \dfrac{180}{\pi}$ degrees, R radians will be $(\dfrac{180}{\pi})R$ degrees; thus the mathematical function that gives D in terms of R is

$$D = \left(\frac{180}{\pi}\right)R.$$

(b) Change R to X and D to Y1, so the function becomes

$$\text{Y1} = \left(\frac{180}{\pi}\right)X \quad \text{or} \quad \text{Y1} = 180X/\pi.$$

When this function is plotted on your calculator, by using a suitable window setting you should obtain a graph similar to the one below.

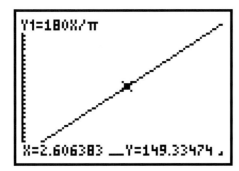

Using the trace facility (see *Calculator Book*, Section 7.2) and the Zoom In or ZBox facilities (see *Calculator Book*, Section 8.5), you should find that the point on the graph with an X-coordinate of about 2.6 has a Y-coordinate of about 149° (to the nearest integer). So an angle of 2.6 radians converts into approximately 149°.

Another approach is to use the table facility of the calculator as shown here.

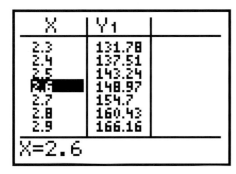

(c) Using the stored function directly (see *Calculator Book*, Section 8.2), you should find that Y1(2.6) gives 149 (to the nearest integer).

Alternatively, to convert 2.6 radians into degrees, put $X = 2.6$. Thus,

$$\text{Y1} = 180 \times 2.6/\pi = 149.$$

This agrees with the approximate result obtained by using the trace and zoom facilities.

(d) Start with the expression for D in terms of R from part (a):

$$D = \left(\frac{180}{\pi}\right)R,$$

and multiply both sides of the equation by π to get

$$\pi D = 180R.$$

Then divide both sides by 180, so

$$\pi D/180 = R,$$

or

$$R = \left(\frac{\pi}{180}\right)D.$$

(e) To make the function you obtained in (d) suitable for inputting into your calculator, change D to X and R to Y2. The function then becomes

$$\text{Y2} = \left(\frac{\pi}{180}\right)X \text{ or } \text{Y2} = \pi X/180.$$

To convert 135° into radians, put $X = 135$, so

$$\text{Y2}(135) = 2.356 \text{ (to 3 d.p)}.$$

(f) As an example, Y1(10) = 572.9577951, and this is stored in Ans. Then inputting the result directly into Y2 gives

$$\text{Y2}(\text{Ans}) = 10.$$

Similarly, Y2(40) = .6981317008. Inputting this result directly into Y1 gives

$$\text{Y1}(\text{Ans}) = 40.$$

In both cases, you end up with your original number.

(g) As you saw in parts (a) and (b), the relationship between the measurement of an angle in degrees and its measurement in radians is of the form:

$$Y = (\text{some number})X.$$

Therefore it is a directly proportional relationship. The graph of the function which expresses such a relationship is a straight line passing through the origin, with the gradient being equal to the constant of proportionality ('some number' in the informal version of the formula!). Thus the gradient of the graph of the function $Y1 = (180/\pi)X$ will be $\frac{180}{\pi}$ or 57.3 (to 1 d.p.), and that of the function $Y2 = (\pi/180)X$ will be $\frac{\pi}{180}$ or 0.017 (to 3 d.p) (see *Unit 7*, Section 1.2).

An alternative way of looking at this question is to recall that the equation of a straight line is of the form $y = mx + c$, where the gradient is m and the y intercept is c. The equations of the functions Y1 and Y2 are both of this form, with the value of c being zero, so they are straight lines with y intercepts of zero. This means that the graphs of both functions cross the y axis where $y = 0$ (and $x = 0$), i.e. at the origin. The gradient of both graphs is m. For the function Y1, m will be $180/\pi$ or 57.3 (to 1 d.p.), and for the function Y2 it will be $\pi/180$ or 0.017 (to 3 d.p.).

Activity 19

(a) Changing A to Y1 and B to X gives the conversion function in a form suitable for inputting into the calculator:

$$Y1 = (5/9)X - 160/9.$$

When this function is plotted on the calculator, by using a suitable window setting you should obtain a graph similar to the one below.

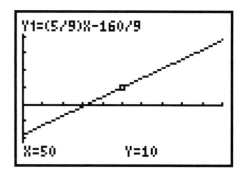

Using the stored function directly to convert $50\,°F$ into Celsius gives $Y1(50) = 10$. So a temperature of $50\,°F$ converts to $10\,°C$.

(b) Substituting $A = 20$ into the conversion function gives $20 = \frac{5}{9}B - \frac{160}{9}$, which can be solved for B. There are several ways of solving the equation, but the principles are the same in all cases. In order to make B the subject of the equation, you need to multiply by 9, divide by 5, and add a constant term. You can do these steps in several different orders (and the constant you add will depend on the order.) Here is one way of doing this:

multiply both sides by 9	$180 = 5B - 160$
add 160 to both sides	$340 = 5B$
divide both sides by 5	$68 = B.$

So a temperature of $20\,°C$ converts to $68\,°F$.

(c) Taking the equation $A = \frac{5}{9}B - \frac{160}{9}$, follow the same sequence of steps as in (b) to make B the subject:

multiply both sides by 9	$9A = 5B - 160$
add 160 to both sides	$9A + 160 = 5B$
divide both sides by 5	$\frac{9}{5}A + 32 = B.$

Thus the equation that gives B in terms of A is

$$B = \tfrac{9}{5}A + 32.$$

To input this function into your calculator, write it in the form:

$$Y2 = (9/5)X + 32.$$

Using the stored function directly gives $Y2(10) = 50$. So a temperature of $10\,°C$ converts to $50\,°F$. This agrees with the conversion 'in the other direction' of $50\,°F$ to $10\,°C$ in part (a).

(d) Function Y2 converts temperatures in degrees Celsius into temperatures in degrees Fahrenheit, and so undoes the conversion that function Y1 does—the two are inverse functions. You can check this in the same way as in Activity 18(f): if you input any value into one of the two functions, and then input the answer you obtain into the other function, you should end up with your original value.

(e) The relationship between the measurement of a temperature on the Celsius scale and its measurement on the Fahrenheit scale is not a *directly* proportional relationship. The relationship is of the form:

$$y = mx + c,$$

which is the equation of a straight line, with c being the y intercept.

For the function Y1,

$$Y1 = (5/9)X - 160/9.$$

Since c is $^-160/9$ rather than zero, the graph of Y1 does *not* pass through the origin. The gradient m is $5/9$.

For the function Y2,

$$Y2 = (9/5)X + 32.$$

The intercept c is 32 rather than zero, so the line does *not* pass through the origin. The gradient is $9/5$ (see *Unit 7*, Section 1.2).

Activity 20

In each of the number games, you build up the formula step by step according to the sequence of instructions, and you can choose whether to simplify your intermediate formula at each stage before performing the next step (see *Unit 8*, Section 1.1) or to leave all the simplifying until last. It is usually easier to simplify as you go along, rather than be faced with dealing with a long complicated expression at the end. So this is the general approach taken here.

(a) Think of a number N
double it $2N$
add 4 $2N + 4$
divide by 2 $N + 2$
take away the number you
first thought of $N + 2 - N$
and the answer is 2, as claimed.

(b) Think of the year in which
you were born Y
subtract it from 2000 $2000 - Y$
and the result is your age in the
year 2000, as claimed, or, more precisely,
*your age on your birthday in the
year 2000*.

(c) Think of a number P
subtract it from 20 $20 - P$
double the result $40 - 2P$
add 5 $45 - 2P$
subtract the number you
first thought of $45 - 3P$
divide by 3 $15 - P$
add the number you
first thought of $15 - P + P$
and the answer is 15, as claimed.

(d) Think of a number M
subtract it from 10 $10 - M$
multiply the result by 3 $30 - 3M$
add 10 $40 - 3M$
subtract the number you
first thought of $40 - 4M$
divide by 4 $10 - M$
subtract the number you
first thought of $10 - M - M$
which gives $10 - 2M.$

So the answer is *not* always 10, as claimed, but it depends on the value of M.

A simple amendment that will make this 'trick' work is to replace the last instruction by '*add* the number you first thought of'; this will have the effect of replacing the last $-M$ in that step by $+M$, so the answer will be 10, as required.

(e)

Think of a positive number	X
subtract 1	$X - 1$
square the result	$(X - 1)^2$
	$= (X - 1)(X - 1)$
	$= X^2 - 2X + 1$
add the number you first thought of	$X^2 - 2X + 1 + X$
	$= X^2 - X + 1$
subtract 1	$X^2 - X$
add the number you first thought of	X^2
take the square root	$\sqrt{X^2} = X$
divide by the number you first thought of	$X/X = 1$
and the answer is	1, as claimed.

(f)

Think of a number	Q
add 2	$Q + 2$
square the result	$(Q + 2)^2$
	$= (Q + 2)(Q + 2)$
	$= Q^2 + 4Q + 4$
subtract 4	$Q^2 + 4Q$
divide by the number you first thought of	$Q + 4$
add the number you first thought of	$2Q + 4.$

So the answer is *not* always 4, as claimed, but it depends on the value of Q.

A simple amendment that will make this 'trick' work is to replace the last instruction by '*subtract* the number you first thought of'. The answer will then be $Q + 4 - Q = 4$, as required.

However, the trick does not work if Q is zero (you cannot divide by zero). So the first line in (f) should say 'Think of a non-zero number'.

Activity 21

(a) The cost to the shopkeeper of X cans of beans at 4 pence per can will be $4X$ pence.

(b) The cost of transport is £10, which is 1000 pence. So the total cost of X cans of beans, including the transport, is $(4X + 1000)$ pence.

(c) If the profit is to be equal to the total cost (including transport), then
total cost + profit = $2 \times$ (total cost).

So, for X cans,
$$\text{total cost} + \text{profit} = 2(4X + 1000) \text{ pence}$$
$$= (8X + 2000) \text{ pence.}$$

The selling price, P pence per can, is the total cost plus profit divided by the number of cans, i.e.
$$P = \frac{8X + 2000}{X}.$$

(d) From part (c),
$$P = \frac{8X + 2000}{X}$$
$$= \frac{8X}{X} + \frac{2000}{X}$$
$$= 8 + \frac{2000}{X}.$$

Note that this equation shows that the selling price of each can is made up of two components: the '8' represents twice the cost price of that can, and the $\frac{2000}{X}$ represents that fraction of twice the transport costs which will need to be covered by the sale of each individual can.

(e) You can plot the graph of this function on your calculator, remembering that since X represents the number of cans and P is the selling price per can, only positive values of X and P are sensible in this context—negative values would make no sense in terms of the real-world situation under consideration. In fact, you need to exercise even further caution, since X and P here represent *discrete variables* (see *Unit 5*, Section 3.1)—the shopkeeper can only buy whole numbers of cans, and sell each can for a whole number of pence. So you will need to round, to the nearest whole number, any values obtained from the function or its graph.

When the function is plotted, by using a suitable window setting you should obtain a graph similar to the one below.

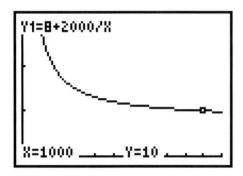

Using the trace facility (see *Calculator Book*, Section 7.2) and Zoom In or ZBox (see *Calculator Book*, Section 8.5), and/or the table facility (see *Calculator Book*, Sections 7.2 and 8.3) gives the following:

(i) When $X = 100$, $P = 28$. So, if the shopkeeper buys 100 cans on the trip to the wholesale market, the selling price must be 28p per can in order to make the required profit.

(ii) When $P = 10$, $X = 1000$. If the shopkeeper wants to be able to sell the cans at only 10p per can and make the required profit, 1000 cans will need to be bought at the wholesale market and then sold.

(f) The function used for the algebraic method is

$$P = 8 + \frac{2000}{X},$$

which you obtained in part (d).

(i) For $X = 100$, this gives

$$P = 8 + \frac{2000}{100}$$
$$= 8 + 20$$
$$= 28.$$

(ii) For $P = 10$, this function gives $10 = 8 + \frac{2000}{X}$, which can be solved for X as follows:

subtract 8 from both sides $2 = \frac{2000}{X}$
multiply both sides by X $2X = 2000$
divide both sides by 2 $X = 1000$.

Note that, in general, you can see from the graph and/or table of values of P as a function of X that:

- The smaller the value of X, the larger the value of P. Taking the real-world extreme value of $X = 1$ gives $P = 2008$.

- If the shopkeeper buys just one can on the trip to the market, the selling price would need to be £20.08 in order to make the required profit, since the whole amount of twice the transport costs will have to be covered by the sale of that single can!

- The larger the value of X, the smaller the value of P, which approaches nearer and nearer to 8. Taking $X = 2000$ gives $P = 9$; thus if the shopkeeper buys 2000 cans, just 1p of the price of each can contributes to twice the transport costs.

Activity 22

As the responses will be very individual, there are no comments on this activity.

Musical glossary

The following musical terms crop up in this unit and are defined briefly here. You are not expected to learn the definitions of these terms, nor will you be tested on them.

bodhrán	(Usually pronounced 'boar-on'.) An Irish drum that is held in one hand and played with a beater.
chromatic scale	A scale consisting entirely of notes one semitone apart. Playing chromatic scales from the bottom of the piano keyboard to the top would take in every note on the keyboard, black and white. See *scale*.
clavier	Another word for 'keyboard'. Spelt 'Klavier', it is the German word for piano.
cycle	If a particular pattern is repeated over and over, one single run of the pattern is called a cycle. (For example, the decimal fraction $\frac{1}{7} = 0.142857142857142857142857\ldots$ has a repeating cycle of the digits 142857.) In the case of a sine curve, one cycle is the wave pattern from one peak to the next peak (or one trough to the next trough).
equally-tempered	The modern method of tuning for most Western instruments, where the intervals between each pair of adjacent semitones are equal.
fifth	An interval of seven semitones; for example, the interval from C up to G, or G up to D. See *interval*.
flat	A flat lowers the note to which it is attached by one semitone. The symbol for a flat is ♭; for example, the note E♭ is one semitone below the note E.
frequency	If a particular pattern is repeated over and over, the rate at which the cycle repeats is the frequency. For example, if a tuning fork, tuned to middle C, is struck, the prongs or tines vibrate with a frequency of 256 cycles per second.
fret	A ridge or bar across the fingerboard of some stringed instruments. The effective length of a string on the instrument can be altered by using a finger to press the string against a fret; thus various fixed notes can be produced when the string is vibrated.
harmony	The combination of two or more notes to produce a pleasing sound. (Notions of harmony can be subjective—a particular combination of notes that sounds harmonious to one person may sound discordant to another.)
interval	The difference in pitch between two notes.

jig A musical form common in folk music and dance, based around a rhythm of six beats grouped in two sets of three. To get an idea of the rhythm of a jig, try saying 'Pine–ap–ple, A–pri–cot' several times.

key A key specifies the notes in a scale. Keys can be major or minor. Tunes are played in particular keys (although the key might occasionally switch in the middle of the tune).

key note Where a tune has been written in a particular key (say, the key of D major), the notes that the tune largely consists of are the notes in the scale of D, namely D, E, F♯, G, A, B, C♯ and D. In this case, D is called the key note, and it is the note that appears to control the tune.

major scale A particular selection of eight notes played in sequence. For example, the scale of C major consists of the notes C, D, E, F, G, A, B and C. See *scale*.

microtone Any interval smaller than a semitone; for example, a quartertone, a sixth of a tone, and so on.

middle C A note commonly used as a reference point. It is found in the middle of a piano keyboard, and has a frequency of 256Hz.

minor scale A particular selection of eight notes played in sequence, which have a sad or wistful quality, often associated with 'the blues'. There are two commonly-used minor scales. The minor scale described in the unit is a simplified version of these forms. See *scale* and *major scale*.

octave An interval of twelve semitones formed by thirteen notes. The thirteenth note sounds the same as the first but is higher in pitch. The first and thirteenth notes are an octave apart. The ratio of the frequencies of notes an octave apart is $\frac{1}{2}$, and the string-length ratio corresponding to an octave is also $\frac{1}{2}$.

oscilloscope A device that records air vibrations (sounds) and displays the resulting patterns on a screen. The basic underlying pattern obtained for a musical note is a sine wave. For high notes, the wave pattern is more bunched up, reflecting the fact that high notes are the result of high-frequency vibrations. On the oscilloscope, each musical instrument will produce its own distinctive pattern which is a particular approximation to a sine wave.

panpipes An instrument made up of a number of small pipes (usually wooden) fastened together. The sound is made by blowing across the top of each pipe—the little pipes produce high notes and the bigger ones the low notes.

pentatonic scale	A simple scale of five notes (or six notes including the closing note). One version of a pentatonic scale is provided by five consecutive black notes played in sequence on a keyboard instrument. The song 'Auld Lang Sang' is based on a pentatonic scale.
pitch	A measure of how high or low a note is. A small whistle or recorder will produce notes that are higher in pitch than a large one.
Pythagorean tuning	The form of tuning for musical instruments that was common in Western music until the beginning of the eighteenth century. It is largely based on the principle that simple fractions lie at the heart of pleasing harmonies.
reel	A musical form common in folk music and dance, based around a rhythm of four beats and usually played fairly quickly. To get an idea of the rhythm of a reel, try saying 'Wa–ter–me–lon' several times.
rhythm	A regular beat or beat pattern, usually applied to music. Different musical styles are characterized by different types of rhythm. See *reel, jig, waltz*.
scale	The sequence of notes that might be played when going from the lowest note of a particular octave to the highest note. The two common types of scale are major and minor.
semitone	The smallest interval commonly used in Western music. A semitone is the gap between two adjacent notes; for example, the interval from C to C♯, or from F♯ to G.
session	An informal musical 'get-together', often associated with Irish music.
sharp	The symbol for a sharp is ♯. A sharp raises the note to which it is attached by one semitone; for example, the note F♯ is one semitone above the note F.
third	An interval of four semitones; for example, the interval from C up to E, or G up to B. See *interval*.
tone	An interval of two semitones; for example, the interval from C to D. (A tone has a second, rather ambiguous, meaning in music, referring to the sound quality of a note.)
tuning fork	A small two-pronged metal device which produces a note of fixed pitch when struck. It is used for tuning musical instruments. The prongs are also known as tines.
waltz	A musical form based around a rhythm of three slow regular beats.

Index